Prince Dimitri's Mountaineers

Prince Dimitri's Mountaineers

Prince Dimitri's Mountaineers

by

Sister Mary Fides Glass

and

Cecilia Glass Bard

ILLUSTRATIONS BY STEPHEN GROUT

Grail Publication

St. Meinrad   Indiana

170653

PREFACE

This is a book of connected stories about old times on the Allegheny Mountains. They are unified because of certain families who are met with in all these tales. These families were close friends of Father Gallitzin; they held his memory in reverence and talked of him to their children and their children's children.

A brief story of Prince Gallitzin is included. He is a tradition on the Alleghenies. He was father and leader of the pioneers and their descendants.

Special interest is given to these stories in the fact that they are true. The characters are real people, some of whose descendants are still living and who agreed that their ancestors and relatives names could be used by the authors. There are a few fictitious names given to characters who have no relatives now known on the mountains.

> Sister M. Fides Glass
> Seton Hill, Greensburg, Pa.
> Cecelia Glass Bard
> Loretto, Pa.

CONTENTS

5

The Prince of the Mountain

PART I

THE PRINCE OF THE MOUNTAIN

SOMETIME you may make a journey to the Allegheny mountains in western Pennsylvania, or visit the foothills of this range in Westmoreland County, which lies about thirty miles east of Pittsburgh.

Some of the country over which you may pass will look almost as it did one hundred years ago: the woodlands, the broad meadows and the rivers; but most of it is completely changed. Smooth two or four lane highways pass through villages that are almost extinct and are so ugly that you have no pity for their being reduced to nothingness. In their last stages they were blots on the landscape with their unpainted houses and wretched bits of gasoline stations, hot-dog stands, billboards on broken-down fences, and garish posters everywhere.

One such village, for which you will have no sympathy, was once called Summitville, on the very top of the Alleghenies. A bit of this village still remains but in a state of delapidation quite unlike its beginning, when the famous Allegheny Portage Railroad crossed the Pittsburgh-Philadelphia Turnpike at the center of the village and everything there was astir.

Before this flowering of Summitville, which was about 1832, it had been one of Prince Gallitzin's missions of his main settlement at Loretto.

Summitville developed because of the railroad which passed through it. It became a rival town to Loretto and had the first post office established on the Allegheny mountains. But Loretto still exists almost the same as in the days of the Prince while Summitville has passed away.

In all probability Loretto shall last as long as the name of Prince Demetrius Gallitzin endures, and his name is likely to glow with more lustre as the years go by. The town as a town may pass away, but the name Loretto as a hallowed shrine and a memorial to the Apostle of the Alleghenies will endure.

Prince Gallitzin was a real prince. He was the last and only son of a noble family of a long line of Gallitzins. His father, Dimitri Alexeievitch Gallitzin, was appointed Ambassador to Holland for Catherine the Great of Russia in 1769. Prince Dimitri had married a German princess, Amalia Von Schmettau, and they were living in Holland when the little Prince was born, December 22, 1770.

Prince Demetrius was carefully educated, because when he would become of age, he was to go to Russia as an important member of the Court of Catherine the Great. Empress Catherine herself had personally bestowed the honor upon the baby prince of becoming her special ambassador.

But when Prince Demetrius reached the age of seventeen he joined the Roman Catholic Church, and a vocation to the priesthood awoke within his soul.

When his schooling was finished, except for a grand tour, which was part of a European gentleman's education in those days, he was sent to the United States of America. France would have been his father's choice for him, but the terrible French Revolutionary War was going on and royal heads were being cut off by the thousands. The Prince would not be safe in France; he might be mistaken for a royal Frenchman.

Prince Demetrius's traveling companion to the United States was a young priest named Father Brosius. From him Demetrius learned of the need of priests in the new country. Father Brosius was alarmed and would tell him no more when he began to read what was in the young Prince's mind. The Prince then kept his secret to himself: he had decided to become a priest in the United States.

Bishop John Carroll had charge of the entire Catholic Church in America; his residence was at Baltimore, Maryland. Prince Gallitzin's ship docked at Baltimore. Father Felix Brosius naturally went to see the bishop to get an appointment. He took the young Prince along.

Prince Demetrius felt that only in the priesthood would his soul be satisfied, and Saint Mary's Seminary, where he stayed, seemed to ease all his heart's cravings. He pleaded with the Bishop to allow him to remain there and begin studying for the priesthood.

After many letters back and forth to his parents he finally received their reluctant consent to follow his vocation. His mother, who had returned to her Catholic faith a year or so before, praised God when she was assured by Bishop Carroll that Prince Demetrius was a very earnest, pious and sincere seminarian. She had doubted his piety and the doubt had troubled her greatly; in reality the young prince was so deeply religious he had never been able to tell anyone but God the thoughts and feelings in his soul.

9

After studying for several years at Saint Mary's Seminary in Baltimore, Prince Gallitzin was ordained there on March 18, 1795.

There was at this time a little settlement on the top of the Allegheny mountains that had been made by Captain Michael McGuire, his sons and their wives and a few other families—about twelve in all.

Captain McGuire, who was a Revolutionary War hero and also a pious Catholic, desired to have a priest permanently settled among his people.

It so happened that the newly ordained Prince, who had been stationed at Conewago in eastern Pennsylvania, was called upon one summer day to make a sickcall to the distant McGuire Settlement on the Alleghenies. There he lived among the people in their own little cabins.

These simple mountaineers had never met his like, for the manners of a real prince shone all about him. When he finally had to return to Conewago they could talk of nothing else but the days when he was with them. They had clustered round him to be married, to go to confession, to have babies baptized, and to go to holy Communion. The sight had touched the young Prince's heart. Everything was just as he had dreamed it on the ship to America. He saw that the people were poor and he knew that he was very rich: he expected some day to be a great deal wealthier. He did not then know that the day could come when enemies in Europe would cheat him out of his inheritance.

When he said goodbye to the mountaineers they begged him to return to them. When he went back to Conewago he could not forget them. A few years later while he was stationed again at Baltimore they petitioned Bishop Carroll to send him to them.

The petition filled the young priest's heart with joy. In a short time he gathered his few belongings, saddled his horse and turned its head northwestward to the Allegheny mountains.

He came to the mountains in August, 1799. The men of the settlement (which the Prince decided to call Loretto in honor of the Blessed Virgin) began building a little log house for his home. Next they built a church. It was finished in time for midnight Mass, Christmas 1799. Prince Gallitzin called the church Saint Michael's.

For many years Saint Michael's was the only Catholic church between Lancaster, Pennsylvania and Saint Louis, Missouri. Later, other settlements grew and the people built their own churches: thus towns began to flourish.

Many settlers came to the mountains because Father Gallitzin helped them financially by selling land to them for less than he had paid for it; he built them a grist mill and a tannery; he taught their children in his school, the first permanent parish school in the United States; he aimed to start a teaching order of Sisters, but God had destined that work for Mother Seton, whom Father Gallitzin afterwards knew very well.

The villages outside of Loretto grew, but many people still went there to church. They walked barefoot on Sundays, carrying their shoes to save them, or they went in rough farm wagons.

Father Gallitzin was still living when the village of Summit had its own church built by the pious settler, Ignatius Adams, whose story you may read later in this book.

Bedford, Newry, Hart's Sleeping Place, Carrolltown and Saint Augustine were the names of some of the towns that began to thrive; they had originally been little missions of Prince Gallitzin.

When the year 1840 arrived Father Gallitzin was a white haired old man, but he had to his credit with God more than six thousand converts to the Catholic faith, and had given the poor more than one hundred fifty thousand dollars. Many young men had been ordained priests and others were looking forward to ordination. The new villages had churches, and in the main the people were very good and faithful Christians.

The dear old Prince-priest, who had struggled through debts, detractions, calumnies, misunderstandings, worry, work, physical accident, terrible pain, fastings, vigils, and long prayers was ready to go to God.

The people had been devoted to the gentle, good old priest, who at times had not failed to scold them, but whose beautiful dark eyes had always shed on them a silent benediction.

It was May 6, 1840, when the Prince died. A few days later he was buried in his own little cemetery close to his new frame church. Hundreds of people from all over the mountain top and down its vast sides gathered for his funeral. Men vied with each other to be his pallbearers; so many claimed this right that he had to be carried all through the village of Loretto with different men taking their turns of a few minutes each to carry him in his casket. When at last he was laid away in his grave the tears of the people were as unceasing as the long spring rains that fall on the mountains. They could not speak of him without weeping.

One of the Prince-priest's earliest biographers, Sara Brownson, (in a book no longer in print) finishes the story thus:

"The sadness of the people when they saw for the first time another in his place did not lessen as the days advanced, however honored his successor.

"Every religious duty required of them, pressed home to them some new phase of their immeasurable loss. Their desolation could not be controlled when they passed his little log cabin, where he no longer sat silent and alone under the great trees, or came with shining eyes to welcome them at his garden gate.

"The recollections of the lovely ways by which he had led their souls to God were never forgotten. Though the silence was never to be broken by that comforting step, he was never absent. In their darkest hours the most forsaken of the mountain folk remembered him and they had sudden glimpses of Heavenly hope and faith, rousing them to courage.

"Death had lost half its terrors since Prince Gallitzin had passed through it. The promised Heavenly reward seemed certain since all his remembered deeds told them that he had surely reached it."

This little story of the Mountain Prince does not begin to tell all there is to be said about him. You must look for his complete history in books entirely dedicated to him. In the tales told here he will be mentioned, because the people of the Allegheny mountains speak of him with reverence and everlasting affection.

PART II

Mount Carmel in the Forest

CHAPTER ONE

LITTLE ANNIE'S CHURCH

*T*HE SOUND of axes could be heard in the woodland around Patrick McDermott's farm in Westmoreland County, Pennsylvania. It was the year 1822 and Pat and his wife had been living there since 1818. They had two children, Catherine, who had been born in Wilmington, Delaware, shortly after Pat and Ann had arrived from Ireland, and James Francis who was five years old.

They had left Wilmington, not because Patrick could not have made a living there as a merchant or weaver (he had been the latter in Ireland), but he had intended on leaving the "ould Country" to find a wee spot in America where they could raise their own potatoes, and have cows and horses and pigs and green fields and all the rest of the things they had always been deprived of.

They had loaded their scanty belongings on pack horses and started out with the Conways, the Murphys, the O'Briens and the McGuires (they were all relatives) across the State of Pennsylvania, over the Allegheny Mountains to the undulating foothills on the

16

western side: Westmoreland, it was called; and indeed there was *more land,* and it was less hilly and forbidding than the mountain tops.

Patrick was pleased with himself, for he had instigated the move. His cabin was up at last. He had left Ann at the McGuire Settlement on the summit of the Alleghenies, while he and the other men went ahead to build the homes. It did not take long, for the cabins were meant to be only temporary. Now all the families were settled, and the next thing they needed was a church; Blairsville Church and Sportsman's hall were too far away.

Father Terrence McGirr, the pastor at Blairsville, had suggested that, with so much timber right at hand, they build their own church. He had seen them come late for Mass several Sundays, when the rough wagon wheels had stuck in the mud.

Now the Irish emigrant farmers were building themselves a temple for God. That is why the axes were ringing in the woods around Patrick McDermott's farm.

James McGuire, Pat's brother-in-law, the richest man among them, who had purchased the greatest amount of land, offered a piece of ground for a site. At a meeting of the men, in McGuire's wide kitchen, they voted Jim McGuire as foreman, "architect", and contractor for the new building. Mr. McGuire was so pleased that his generosity was roused to a higher pitch and he offered a large strip of ground for a cemetery as well.

Wouldn't it be fine to have a church in their midst! The blessing of God would come down upon them all. Christ Himself would be their King and protect them in this wilderness. They could stop in the church and pray of an evening after their work was done. Their

17

babies would be baptized there, and when they themselves died, they would be buried in the shade of its sanctuary. Perhaps in days to come there might be a grand large church replacing this small log one, and their graves would be tended and their souls prayed for constantly.

It was thus that James McGuire and his wife Catherine talked together when they decided to give the land to Father McGirr. Their little daughter, Annie, aged six, standing by, took the conversation in.

For awhile the Irish Settlement could talk of nothing else but the building of the church. John and Unity Conway, who had come over the Alleghenies at the same time, and who now lived at Livermore, some miles away, came to visit the McDermotts and to discuss the matter. Nobody was to receive any pay for his labor on the church; it was "our" church and everybody had an intense interest in its construction.

But in the McGuire cabin there was one member of the family who was more deeply interested in the erection of the church than anybody in the entire settlement. Little Annie McGuire had it constantly in mind. She watched the stones laid for the foundation; she stood by and got in the way when the huge logs were being hoisted into place. She was everywhere at once in the vicinity of the new building.

"It's my church," said Annie to her aunt, Mrs. McDermott, "daddy says it's mine; he is building it specially for me, and he wants me to pray every day to the Blessed Virgin that it will be a good church and that God will like it."

"Well, I hope you pray to the Blessed Virgin that we can have the priest often to say Mass for us. Priests are scarcer here than they were in Ireland," said Mrs. McDermott.

"I'll pray for everything we need," answered Annie. She needed no advice in her praying: she knew the "Our Father" and the "Hail Mary" and she had a rosary of her own that had been brought from Ireland; there were a few beads missing for Annie knew there should be ten beads to a decade; she could count to ten easily. She could even spell and read a little; daddy had taught her.

Every day since the day on which she had fallen into the mortar, she sat on a stump in the woods and watched the farmers at work on the church. She saw them shape the corners of the logs and fit them together; she prudently came closer and watched the mortar being put between the logs. She chatted with the farmers and told them that it was her church. They agreed that it was. Annie carried her rosary with her, and when she wasn't saying it she placed it round her neck, and carefully crawled over the sawdust piles and peeped about at everything.

Each day at dawn Annie was up. She stayed at the church all day, unless her mother kept her inside to sew carpet rags or to rock the baby; but as soon as these duties were done, away she went to see how her church was getting on. On wet days she asked her father many questions.

The church was going up fast and would soon be ready for a roof. It was springtime and the ploughing and sowing went on as usual, but there was always someone at the work of carpentering for the church. In the long evenings every man lent a hand.

Suddenly little Annie McGuire was very much bothered about her church. One day she heard her mother say to her father: "Jim, what Saint is Father McGirr going to call the church after? It has to have a Saint to protect it, you know."

19

Her father had answered: "Sure, I guess Father Terrence'll have a name thought out by the time it's ready to be dedicated—that is, if he doesn't forget. He's a great one to be forgetting things."

That was exactly what bothered Annie: Father Terrence would forget to select a name for the church, and it would stand there for years and years without a name, and with no saint of its own to care specially for it. It would soon be ready to be dedicated and nobody had taken up the question of a name.

Annie sat on the edge of her trundle bed in the cabin corner, before she crawled under the quilt, and pondered the matter:

"There's Saint Anne," she meditated, "Saint Anne watches over me—she was the Blessed Virgin's mother and watched over her, too. I like Saint Anne—she was little Jesus' grandmother. Saint Catherine watches over my Ma and Saint James over Daddy. We have many people from heaven to take care of us, and my church will have nobody for a long time—if Father Terrence forgets." Next morning Annie decided to take her problem to her mother.

"Ma, what name would be nice for my church, when it is all built?" she asked.

"Oh, I guess Father McGirr will have a name ready when it's time," her mother replied.

"He might forget," said Annie, with a worried expression on her face. "He forgets things often. He forgot the big book one Sunday and Daddy had to lend him his little one; he forgot the candlesticks and you had to go home and get ours. He might forget to name my church."

"You mustn't criticise the priest, Annie, it's bad luck. Father McGirr has a lot of things on his mind, with three places to tend to, on Sundays."

"I know, Ma, that's why I think we should help him out and tell him a nice name."

"Now, Annie," said Mrs. McGuire, exasperated, "you stop bothering so much about the church; say your prayers and leave the name to the priest."

Annie pushed her trundle bed under the big one in which her parents slept, and said in a sad mumble from underneath:

"But he might give it a name that I don't like—and it's *my* church. He might call it Saint 'Turrence', and I don't like 'Turrence.' " Annie crawled out from under the bed: "Is there a Saint 'Turrence', Ma?" she said.

Mrs. McGuire lost her patience. She looked about for something to do with this little pest, and then she saw the chickens in the garden.

"For gracious sakes, Annie," she shrieked in relief, "the chickens have gotten out and are scratching up my beans. Hurry and chase them. Jim has left the gate open."

Annie shot out the door and downstairs; the subject was disposed of that day for Mrs. McGuire, but not for Annie. She sat down under the grapevine on an old wooden stool, after a successful chase of the chickens. She would think of names for her church all day between the intervals of chasing the energetic hens. They would have to be watched every minute, for it was impossible to get them back in the pen once they had their freedom in the garden; handfuls of corn would not entice them when they could scratch out a fresh bean for themselves. Dry corn was all right for winter, but this was springtime and green gardens were delightful places for roosters to crow and for hens to scratch in.

21

Annie rocked herself on her stool and sighed, while she kept one eye on "Black Polly", the sneakiest pullet of all. "Saint Mary, for the Blessed Virgin. Blessed Virgin Church." In her imagination Annie was down at the church now. "St. Catherine's Church, for Ma. Saint Annie Church, for God's grandmother and for me, too. Saint Patrick's Church for uncle Pat McDermott. Saint Unity's Church for Unity Conway. Unity?" It was a queer name! "Unity?" Oh, horrors! Black Polly was in the beans!

CHAPTER TWO

ANNIE HAS A VISITOR

*I*N JULY 1822 "the church" was finished. It was still called "the church"; no grown-up member of the congregation was concerned about a name. To have Mass in their midst was such joy that nothing else mattered.

Father McGirr was around quite often now. One day Annie heard him speaking of "the church". He had not given the church a name! Annie hurried quickly to where her father was working.

"Pa," she said eagerly, "come, and ask Father McGirr what he is going to name my church?"

"Is Father here?" asked Mr. McGuire, putting down a plank. "Sure I've been wanting to see him about the cross on the gable. Where is he, Annie?"

"He's around in front. Oh, daddy, ask him about the name!" Annie's little face was puckered with anxiety.

Mr. McGuire paid no heed. He was more interested in seeing that the cross was fitted correctly on the gable. When he was satisfied with Father McGirr's answers, he remembered Annie's question.

"Oh, by the way, Father, what name will you give our church? My little Annie is bothered about its name."

"Oh, a name is it?" said Father McGirr abstractedly, while Annie drew near and watched him with wide eyes. "Sure, we can think of that later; there'll be plenty of time to name it later." And Father McGirr changed the subject.

Annie was too shy to talk up to the priest and beg for a name. She walked sadly away, twisting her apron corner into a tight little knot. The church was to be nameless for a long time, just as she had feared. A name didn't matter to Father "Turrence." There would be no special saint chosen to watch over *her* church. Maybe the guardian angels of all the people would undertake the job, if she asked them. Well, that would be the best she could do.

Annie went home and told her mother that Father McGirr said a name for the church didn't matter for a long time.

"Well, Annie, I hope you are satisfied," said Mrs. McGuire.

Annie went to bed that night with an ache in her soul, or her heart, or her stomach; she couldn't locate it. She wasn't exactly sick but she felt very sad; it was almost like being sick, only it was worse. If you had the stomach-ache for sure, you could take peppermint or catnip and pretty soon you were well again; if you had the headache, you could tie a horse-radish leaf on your forehead and it would be cured in a jiffy. But this sort of sad sickness, that Annie had now, resisted medicines. Only something to make you happy could cure it. Annie was afraid that her sad sickness would last until her church was given a beautiful name.

24

Annie thought of Father Gallitzin. Sometimes he visited the people at the farms. He was so nice and kind; she could talk to him. But this wasn't *his* church, he couldn't give it a name.

Annie had been disappointed in Father Gallitzin the first time she saw him. Ma had said that he was a Prince. Annie had expected to see a Prince like the one in the story of Cinderella. Ma had said that he was a priest, too, but being a Prince, Annie had thought that he would be dressed in silk and velvet, and have big plumes in his hat. Ma said he owned castles and palaces and bags of money in his native country, and that sometime he was to get them all. But life was full of delusions for Annie; the first time she saw Father Gallitzin, he was no Prince to her way of thinking. He was just a plain priest with an old black hat—no plumes at all—he wore a patched cassock, and his thick-soled shoes were muddy. Annie had stood gaping at him, almost ready to cry over her disappointment. But she didn't tell her thoughts and when he spoke to her and talked so nicely about God and the angels and the Blessed Mother, she forgot all about princes and princesses and was glad that Father Gallitzin was a plain priest. He was not gruff like Father McGirr.

Annie knelt by her bed and said the last decade of her rosary. It was dark in the room when she crawled into her trundle bed. Ma and Daddy would come to bed later but Annie would not hear them; she would be sound asleep. She would sleep until broad daylight. The sun always came up on her side of the room, and looked right in the window. It was the sunlight that wakened Annie each morning: it shone right on her closed eyelids and she seemed to see its beams through them.

Annie pulled the calico quilt up to her chin, then she turned over on her side and clutched the cross of her rosary, which was round her neck. She turned her back to the window so that when morning came she wouldn't see the sun until its beams shot right across the pillow and found her eyes. Her last thought was of her church. It would be nameless for years. Annie said a final Hail Mary and closed her eyes.

She loved the Blessed Mother very much. She called her "Dear Blessed Virgin" and "dear Mother of God." She had never heard any other titles, such as "Our Lady of Good Counsel", or "Our Lady of Sorrows", "Lady of Mercy" and other beautiful titles: she was just the Blessed Virgin or God's Mother to little Annie.

It was dark and quiet in the room; Annie was asleep. Suddenly it was morning! Annie's eyes flew wide open. She sat up in bed. Where was she? Had she died and gone to Heaven? The room was lit so brightly she couldn't see anything in it, and there right beside Annie's trundle bed stood a wonderful lady. Annie knew her right away. "Oh," she said, "you are the Blessed Virgin!" The Lady, in the middle of the brightness, nodded her head and smiled. Annie folded her hands as she did in prayer and looked at her. "Oh, my, but you are pretty," she said. "Are you going to take me to Heaven?" The Lady shook her head slowly and Annie knew she meant that she wasn't going to take her yet.

"Oh, I know!" exclaimed Annie, delightedly, "you are going to name my church."

The Lady smiled, as if to say: "You have guessed correctly."

Then the Lady spoke. She said: "You, Annie, are to give the church a name that I will tell you. It is to

be called the church of Our Lady of Mount Carmel. I am the Lady of Mount Carmel, and you must tell Father McGirr that I want the church called by that name."

"Our Lady of Mount Carmel!" repeated Annie, with astonishment.

"Say it again," said the shining, beautiful Lady.

"Our Lady of Mount Carmel," repeated obedient Annie. "Once more," said the Lady.

"Our Lady of Mount Carmel," said Annie for the third time.

"Now you will not forget it; tell Father McGirr as soon as possible. Lie down now and go to sleep; it is a long time until morning."

Annie pulled up the quilt again and crawled under the covers.

In no time it was real morning and Annie remembered: "Our Lady of Mount Carmel," she said. "Oh, wasn't she pretty? Wasn't she the prettiest lady anyone could ever see; prettier than a Princess in a Cinderella story. And she was the Blessed Virgin. She took all my sadness away."

Annie went down the rough stairway in a daze. Her mother was out in the spring-house churning; Annie could hear the squeak of the churn handle. Daddy had gone to the wheat fields for it was after eight o'clock. Her mother had baby Tom's cradle in the shade of a tree near the spring-house door.

Annie saw all these ordinary things without thinking about them; Her thoughts were centered on her dream or vision during the night. Without stopping to get any breakfast she ran out and down to her mother.

"Oh, Ma!" she exclaimed, "I know the name of the church."

Her mother stopped churning, and looked at her queerly. "What,—what are you saying, Annie?" she asked.

Annie rushed to her mother's side. "I saw the Blessed Virgin, Ma, and she told me the name for my church." Annie clasped her hands and looked up into her mother's wondering face. "Our Lady of Mount Carmel told me the name, that's to be the name, Ma, 'Our Lady of Mount Carmel', the Blessed Virgin herself said so."

Mrs. McGuire's amazement and surprise lessened, and once again she grew provoked at Annie.

"Are you still talking about a name for the church? I'm afraid you are a little bit crazy. If you've had your breakfast you can come out here and help me with the churning. Have you had your breakfast?"

"No, Ma, not yet, I wanted to tell you first about seeing the Blessed Virgin. Oh, Ma, it wasn't a dream; I saw her and she said I was to call the church 'Our Lady of Mount Carmel'. She made me say it three times, she did, so's I'd remember it. Then she said, 'Lie down and go to sleep, it is a long time until morning.' "

Mrs. McGuire had stopped churning and was listening with bewilderment. She wanted Annie to be good. She, herself, had taught her her prayers and had told her stories of the Saints and angels, but she had never expected her to take religion so seriously!

"What else?" said Mrs. McGuire, sternly, but eager, nevertheless, to hear how far Annie would go with this illusion.

Annie twisted her hands nervously—she was afraid of her mother when she looked so cross. "The Blessed Virgin said I was to tell Father McGirr as soon as I could. Just as soon as possible. Oh, it's true, Ma, I saw her." Annie dropped her hands and waited for a sound scolding.

"Go to the house and get your breakfast, then come out here and help me!" snapped her mother. Annie turned and ran.

But poor Mrs. McGuire wasn't taking Annie and her story so lightly as that. She was bothered about her: Annie must be taking some serious disease; she had talked in her sleep a great deal last night, and she surely must be either delirious or "touched in the head" to tell a dream like that and think it true! Mrs. McGuire felt she must tell her husband about it; it was he who had put it into Annie's head in the first place that the church was hers.

It was time to give the chickens their breakfast and as Annie was getting her own breakfast late, Mrs. McGuire went to perform this chore herself. Tommy was sleeping soundly in his cradle under the tree; she turned to look at him, when she caught sight of Mr. McGuire coming up the lane from the wheatfield. She beckoned to him as he was about to go to the barn; he came towards her and when he saw the anxious expression on her face he said:

"Why, what's wrong, Katie?"

"It's Annie, Jim," she said, "She must be going to have a spell of sickness. She talked a lot in her sleep last night, but I couldn't make a word of it out. This morning she insists that she saw the Blessed Virgin who told her a name for the church. I guess it was a nightmare she had; but I don't like the way she is taking on about that church; maybe she is touched in the head. She says the Blessed Virgin told her the church is to be called 'Our Lady of Mount Carmel'. Now where would she, at her age, hear a name like that? Have you been telling her stories?"

30

James McGuire looked puzzled. "No, Katie, I never told her anything like that. Where'd she ever get such an idea? Father Terrence never takes time to talk to her, except to ask her if she can bless herself; he doesn't expect much of children. She is too little to have read it. Maybe she did see God's Mother, Katie. She is a good little thing."

"Now don't be silly, Jim; it's a dream, and nothing else. She was restless last night. Or maybe she's losing her mind, that's what's worrying me most. She never stops talking about the church."

"I'm going up to the house now, Katie, for some of that popcorn seed. I'll see what I can get out of Annie. But don't you worry; there's not much in this wilderness to amuse a child all by herself; these farms are too far apart. If I think Annie is sick I'll hitch up and take her to Blairsville to the doctor." Mrs. McGuire returned to her churning.

When Mr. McGuire came in the door Annie was clearing the kitchen table and getting ready to wash the dishes. Sis Weaver would be around later from the next farm to help with the canning of strawberries. Annie always had the dishes done and the kitchen set to rights before Sis arrived; Annie was a good little housekeeper for her six years.

"Well, Annie," said Mr. McGuire, "your Ma says you are not so well. She says you talked a lot in your sleep last night. What's the matter girlie?" Mr. McGuire put his hand on her forehead.

Annie looked surprised.

"I'm not sick, pa," she answered quickly. "I'm not a bit sick. I'm just sort of mixed up in my mind"; and Annie rubbed her brow from which her father had just removed his hand. "I'm sure I saw the Blessed

31

Virgin last night and she told me a name for the church, but Ma thinks I just had the nightmare. But I did see the Blessed Virgin and she said I'm to call the church 'Our Lady of Mount Carmel.'"

Mr. McGuire took Annie's hand and felt her pulse; it was regular and normal.

"What did you eat for supper last night, Annie, that made you dream such things as that?" he asked smiling.

"We had strawberry short-cake and potatoes and lamb stew. It was a good supper and didn't make me sick at all."

"Well, who ever told you that the Blessed Virgin had a name like that? Did Father Gallitzin tell you?"

"Oh no, Pa, Father Gallitzin told me about the Blessed Virgin's house that the angels carried on their wings across the sea, when bad people were going to steal it. The angels put it in a place named Loretto, and he calls his town that, and he calls his church Saint Michael's, after God's principal angel. You were listening when he told that story to Ma and me. He never told me about a Carmel church. I don't know why the Blessed Virgin likes that strange name. Do you, daddy?"

"No, I don't, Annie, but I want to tell you something." Mr. McGuire was serious now for he saw that Annie was deeply impressed by her dream or vision or whatever it was. It would not be right to scold her or to pass it off lightly; she would only brood over it in silence and then it would have a bad effect.

"Sit down here, Annie, on this bench, and we'll talk this thing over." Annie laid the tea towel on the table and seated herself; Mr. McGuire sat down beside her, crossed his knees and leaned over and looked at her, just as he did when he was talking to uncle Pat or one of the farmers. Annie liked to be talked to this way: it made her feel grown-up and important.

"You know, Annie," began her father, "sometimes the bad man puts queer notions into people's heads just to fool them. The bad man was once a bright angel in Heaven. His name was Lucifer, which means bright light. Well, he wouldn't obey God and he got put out of Heaven and sent down to the bad place; he has been terribly spited ever since and he likes to fool people, hoping that when he has them fooled, he can get them in his power and away from God. So you must not let him fool you. He can make himself look like a beautiful angel again, but he isn't one at all, at all."

Annie was listening intently; she answered her father by saying:

"Daddy, it was a bright light that wakened me; she was standing right in the light and she was shining, too. I sat up in bed and started to talk to her."

"I think it was only a very strong dream, Annie, and you must try to forget it; you mustn't talk so much about the church or bother your head what the priest calls it. It worries your mother."

"But," said Annie, "I don't think it was Lucifer I saw, because I had my rosary round my neck, and I sprinkled holy water before I went to bed. Lucifer can't come near you when you do that."

"That's right, Annie, he can't, and so it must have been a dream. I must go back to the field." Mr. McGuire stood up. "Promise me to not think about it any more, Annie."

Annie got up too, and picked up the tea towel again. "Daddy I'll try to not think of it," she said.

CHAPTER THREE

ANNIE NAMES HER CHURCH

*J*AMES McGUIRE was satisfied that little
Annie was neither ill nor losing her mind;
she had just had a very vivid dream. He
told his wife all about his talk with their
little girl and she was also relieved.

But all that day and on the one following, Annie was
silent and thoughtful. She still remembered the name,
"Our Lady of Mount Carmel." A whole day of chasing
Black Polly out of the garden, for she had sneaked out
of the pen again, as well as work in the strawberry
patches, had not dimmed the brightness of Annie's
dream or vision.

Mrs. McGuire realized that Annie was not in the
least ill: she had slept well on the following nights, but
on the third day she brought the subject up again.

"Ma," she said, "day after tomorrow will be Sunday.
If Father 'Turrence' comes, you will tell him about
what the Blessed Virgin said to me?"

Mrs. McGuire tucked the quilt into the corner of the
bed she was making, thumped the pillows and put
them in place before she spoke. She was thinking....
Annie had not mentioned the subject since her father

had talked with her and told her that maybe the bad man was up to his tricks. Evidently she had not dropped the subject at all. There was only one thing to do: take her to the priest and have him bless her!

"Father McGirr will be at the church on Sunday, Annie," she said, "and I will take you into the sacristy after Mass. You can tell him yourself."

"Oh, he scares me, Ma,—*you* tell him." pleaded Annie.

"No, I won't, you'll just have to get over being afraid of him. I don't put any stock in that story of yours— maybe if you get the priest's blessing, you'll forget it."

"All right, Ma, I'll tell him, but I don't want to *ever* forget what I saw."

When Sunday arrived Mrs. McGuire took her small daughter into the sacristy of the new log church. Mass was just over and Father McGirr was pulling the vestments off as fast as possible, and with enough tugs and jerks to tear them to pieces. His broad face was protruding from a twisted, long linen alb, when Mrs. McGuire and Annie appeared at the sacristy door.

"Good morning, Mrs. McGuire!" he bellowed jovially and beamed all over. Now he was out of the alb and he gave it a fling to the open window sill. "Come in. Come in." he shouted.

Mrs. McGuire shoved Annie forward, saying: "Father, would you please give my little girl your blessing with the holy water; she's been seeing things at night and sleeping badly. Sure and I think a priest's blessing would be good for her. If you'll just lay your blessed hand on her head and sprinkle her with the holy water a bit, it might cure her, it might."

Annie saw that she must speak up, for her mother was omitting the most important matter.

"Father Turrence, I saw the Blessed Virgin," she piped, "and she says this church is to be called 'Our Lady of Mount Carmel.' I saw her, I did, and I can't forget it, no matter how many 'Hail Marys' I say."

Father McGirr looked down at Annie. He wrinkled his face and opened his mouth in surprise. Who was this midget, with her bright grey eyes and her head cocked on one side, talking up to him?

"What's that? What's that you say?" he asked quickly, and cocking his head, too, as if he thought that his ears had deceived him. But he had heard very well what Annie had said.

"The Blessed Virgin wants this church named 'Our Lady of Mount Carmel,'" said Annie very clearly and decidedly; she was not a bit afraid of Father McGirr now that she had started to talk. She thought he looked sort of scared of her; she'd keep him scared, so she pursued the subject and emphasized it: "The Blessed Virgin told me to tell *you* that *you* are to call this church *after her*. I saw her standing in a big light and she made me say 'Our Lady of Mount Carmel' three times, so that I wouldn't forget it."

Mrs. McGuire was suddenly overcome with timidity at the assurance of Annie; she stood right back of her looking so meek and apologetic one would have thought she had been guilty of insulting a holy man of God. But for once a small child had Father McGirr's complete attention.

"'Our Lady of Mount Carmel' is it?" said he. "Well, that wouldn't be such a bad name. We're up here on top of a hill. Sure that name will do finer than any I know, but a name is the least of me troubles; I'll write it down here and when the bishop comes I'll give it to him, and ye can begin calling the church that if ye like it."

Father McGirr turned to a blank page of the missal and wrote "Our Lady of Mount Carmel." Then he turned to Mrs. McGuire and paid no further attention to Annie: "Will you tell your man, Mrs. McGuire, that the wind has blown the cross on the gable a bit crooked; I guess we better not have such a high one after all. He better put up the one he wanted at first. I shouldn't o'been dictatin' to an 'architect.'" Father McGirr grinned slyly, but it was lost on Mrs. McGuire, for she hadn't accomplished her aim yet.

"Father, will ye bless Annie?" she petitioned humbly.

"Oh yes, yes—'tis sprinkled ye want. I about forgot." With that Father McGirr snatched the sprinkler from the aspersorium and doused Annie with almost enough holy water to drown her; then he laid a heavy hand on her head for a second, and finished by cutting in the air over her, a sign of the cross almost as large as the one he had affixed to the gable of the new log church. Then he seemed to realize that he had "wasted" a lot of time: "Is that all ye wanted, Mrs. McGuire?" he asked with his usual gruffness.

She stepped out of the sacristy backwards pulling Annie with her in the same position. Then they turned and hastily left the church, looking as though they had stolen something.

Father McGirr hurried over the hill to Blairsville where he had another Mass to say. When he turned round to preach he remembered that the new mission church was finished out at the Irish Settlement, and he told them that its name was to be 'Our Lady of Mount Carmel.' After that it didn't need to wait for a bishop to name it formally. Before the day closed almost every Catholic for miles around was talking about Our Lady of Mount Carmel and wondering why

the church had not been given a good Irish Saint's name instead.

Now whether little Annie McGuire saw the Blessed Virgin or not will never be known on earth.

If you would like to see what remains of Annie's church you had better make a trip within the next few years, for it is fast falling to decay; sad to say, it is now, not much more than a pile of blackened logs. Annie's grave is nearby, and that of her father and mother and those of Patrick and Anne McDermott with their son, James Francis, between them. Alas, they are all forgotten; their tombstones are either fallen flat or are covered with weeds and briars. No one prays for their souls in a grand new temple, or even in a little shrine, in that spot where it may really be that our Blessed Lady once visited. Perhaps she came specially for those good people, watched over them, took them to Heaven and then departed herself, to come no more to Old Mount Carmel in the forest of Westmoreland.

PART III

Michael Dan's Epitaph

MICHAEL DAN'S EPITAPH

A Story Founded on Facts of the Time of
Father Gallitzin.
1937

ICHAEL DAN MAGEGAN was bursting with rage as he gave Father Gallitzin's doorknocker a second impatient and resounding knock. He took off his high topper and mopped his brow, although it was a cool morning in early November. He glanced again at the editorial page of "The Mountaineer" which he held in his hand, as he heard the bolt of the door being lifted from the inside of the log house. Father Gallitzin himself opened the door.

"Good morning, Father," said Michael Dan as he rushed into the house before the priest had time to lean the huge iron bar in the corner behind the door, and before Michael was invited, or even greeted.

"I want you to see this, I do!" he shouted. "I want you to read with your own two eyes the impudence of that divil of a Conway. Now just read *that*, will ye?" Magegan thrust the paper into the priest's hands while he pointed with an irate and shaking finger to an item printed therein.

Father Gallitzin took the journal, and after leaning the door-bar in the corner, he laid a firm hand on the shoulder of Michael Dan.

"Now calm yourself, Michael," he said, "calm yourself; you're in a terrible rage so early in the morning. It is bad for the health of your soul and body. Come in the room and sit down, but I'll not read a word of what is here, until you have cooled off. Don't you know, Michael, it is a sin to be so angry with your neighbors, just for your own selfish interests? I guess this is politics again? Now take this easy chair; I keep it for such occasions; and come back to your senses."

Father Gallitzin still held the paper, while he almost pushed the angry, stocky little Irishman into the big armchair by the low window.

But Michael Dan was not to be quelled so easily, nor would he be seated; he was on his feet and snatching for the paper.

"Read it!" he yelled. "Shure and if ye read it, ye'll see I've good cause for bein' in a towerin' rage. That whippersnapper has printed a horrible piece about me in his low-down paper. He thinks he's a great poet, he does, the cursed Democrat. I'll consign him to hell, I will, and all his tribe. You can't take his part this time. He thinks he's funny. Well, I'll make him laugh on the other side of his mouth with his poetry—the low-down Orangeman."

Father Gallitzin saw that he would have to use strong means to settle this wild storm of vituperation and anger. He stood head and shoulders above Michael, and now he straightened himself as much as his old age would allow and planted himself before Michael Dan's chair. He pointed to the door.

"There's the door Michael. Now get out at once if you don't intend to control yourself. You are fit for the insane asylum. I'll not read a line of what Conway has written, unless you sit in that chair and behave like a gentleman. Now either cool off or get out!"

Michael Dan sat down with a thump. He was breathing hard and his hat was still on his head, pushed back from his perspiring brow. He took the hat off and put it on the floor beside him; he stuffed his red bandana handkerchief back in his pocket.

Father Gallitzin took a seat near him by his own neatly arranged desk and unfolded the paper. It was "The Cambria Mountaineer" of which William Bernard Conway was proprietor and editor.

" 'Tis that poetry there", said Magegan, as he saw the priest scanning the page. "Right there in the most prominent place; that 'Epitaph' there, and me not even dead." And Michael Dan folded his arms across his heaving chest, squared his jaw and boiled interiorly for a more just explosion, when Father Gallitzin should have read and agreed with him about the lines.

Father Gallitzin then saw the heading: "Epitaph", and underneath this misleading title, the following doggerel:

> Here lie the political bones of a man,
> Who once was a libeller's attorney:
> His first name was michael, his second was dan,
> And his life was a mutable journey.

The Prince-priest noticed that Conway had spelled Magegan's name with small letters. He continued reading:

> He added to law the congenial adjunct
> Of changing political science,
> Yet nevertheless the great libellant defunct
> On changes placed solid reliance.

His long noisy speeches were uttered with force,
Though his arguments wandered at random,
His tastes were his own and peculiarly coarse,
But degustibus nil disputandum.

The constant mutations of things here below,
All human relations estranging,
Put the tide of his mind in an ebb and a flow
Which kept him eternally changing.

And when his bright hopes by the fiat of fate
Were reduced to a few dying cinders,
On a character then he would fain speculate
Which his folly had shattered to flinders.

For truth though as simple and cogent and clear
As the holy contents of the Bible,
In his understanding would somehow appear
In the horrible garb of a libel.

All parties had witnessed this wandering star,
As he passed through the infinite phases,
As bright as the end of a mammoth cigar,
Still shining and blowing like blazes.

This light is eclipsed—in the grave he is crammed,
Where political changes have thrown him,
A gone politician, he's dead and he's damned,
So de mortuis nil nisi bonum.
                              —W. B. Conway.

Father Gallitzin could scarcely suppress a smile
when he had finished reading; but he wouldn't dare.
It was a difficult job to be friends with two deadly enemies; two Catholics, and both of them his spiritual
children, although they no longer lived in his parish,
but in adjoining ones: Michael Dan at St. Patrick's at
Summitville and William Conway at Ebensburg.

He read the doggerel over again for Michael Dan was
becoming quiet.

Father Gallitzin knew Conway well and was very fond of him; their political views were not the same, but it was not on political grounds that he favored him, his affection rested on something of much more value than politics.

Michael Dan had instinctively felt that Father Gallitzin liked Conway better than he did him, and it made him hate his political opponent all the more, with a very personal and human grudge.

To Michael there was something in this dastardly doggerel that would show the Prince-priest what sort of a viper he had been hob-nobbing with.

Father slowly folded the paper and held it in his hand while he lifted his eyes to Michael Dan to give him his opinion and advice. He knew that Conway had erred in writing the piece, and he would speak to him also. But he understood that it did not contain the vindictiveness that Magegan attributed to it. Conway was a puckish fellow and his humor went astray at times.

"Now listen to me, Michael," began Father Gallitzin to the now quietly heaving Irishman, "I want you to pay no attention to this piece of cockiness at all. Just ignore it. William has done it to stir you up, and you will satisfy him greatly by reacting just as he expected—so fool him this time. Did you ever notice how he sometimes ignores his opponents? They invite him to meetings and he never shows up; then they whoop, howl and rage and his friends tell him all about it. He goes off chuckling and the next week he puts something in his paper about them. Why do the Whigs give him a chance? You have no paper, and where only a few can hear you, hundreds can read what he prints. Now hear me out, Michael, and don't interrupt me. Just ignore this piece of bad poetry; tell all your friends to do the same. I will speak to William. I will give him a piece of my mind; he has used his paper to take advantage of you. But I don't want you to try to get even. Not with a bit of nonsense like this."

"Nonsense, do you call it. 'Tis worse than nonsense," gasped the slowly cooling-off Michael; "why Father, he makes me the laughing stock of this mountain; and he's got such a great followin' now, usin' his derisive ways against me, with his Frinch and his Latin, and his trips to Washington to visit Jackson and Van Buren. And now with this poetry belittlin' me, I'll stand no chance at the elections at all, at all." Michael Dan picked up his hat.

"I might o' known better than to come here," he said as he arose, "I might o' known you wouldn't get very mad at him. Ye tell me to hold onto me tongue and to keep cool to spite him. Shure, he'd think he'd conquered me. I guess 'tis because you're a frind of Conway. He's insulted me, he has. I've heard that ye lean to his ideas yourself. If you give me me paper I'll be goin', but I'll get even with Conway for this." Michael Dan placed his hat on the back of his head and reached to take the paper out of the priest's hand. But Father Gallitzin held him off.

"Now Michael Dan," he remonstrated in firm tones, "you know you are speaking unjustly about me; surely you realize that I've always treated you and William Conway the same. I'm just as much interested in your welfare as I am in his; politics have nothing to do with it. Why can't you learn to separate your political views from your personal feelings? Fight Conway all you want on your different political platforms, uphold your opinions all you wish, if you sincerely think they are for the common welfare, but why can't you remember that you are a Christian? If Conway beats you in a contest, why, lose like a brave soldier, instead of snarling and biting."

" 'Snarling and biting,' is it ye say? I knew ye were for him. That settles it. 'Tis not long since that I heard that he called me a 'cur',—and now you, yourself say that I snarl and bite; give me my paper and I'll be biddin' ye the time o' day."

Michael Dan snatched the paper from Father Gallitzin and fairly flew out the door, hurtling it back on its heavy hinges and slamming it after him till the log house shook and all the little window panes rattled.

Father Gallitzin looked after him in dismay and waited till the echoes of his departure had fallen into stillness. Then he moved closer to the desk and leaned his head on his hand to give himself up to pondering.

" 'Snarling and biting,' " he murmured, "I should not have said that—it stirred him up all over again. Oh, what shall I do with these antagonistic Irishmen? Oh, these Irish; what an attachment and a trial they are for me. But Conway is right: Magegan does act like a little cur sometimes; he won't quietly listen to reason, but there's good in the man. He has a good heart, and is kind to the poor, but just now politics have him warped beyond himself. Will I ever be able to bring about a reconciliation between him and William Conway?" Father Gallitzin's thoughts then turned towards Magegan's enemy.

"William Bernard Conway—an ardent, brilliant and loveable genius. If I could only break him of that whimsical trait of poking satirical fun at his opponents. I must go and see Conway and reprimand him for that doggerel in his paper. Oh, William, why will you not 'let sleeping dogs lie?' I'm afraid you'll get badly bitten sometime, perhaps even mauled to death by a pack of angry wolves. If only you'd let

politics alone and devote yourself to law and literature..."

Father Gallitzin raised his eyes to the crucifix above
his desk and sat looking at it for a long quiet five
minutes. Then he arose and went to the door that
Magegan had so shortly since slammed in his wrath.
He opened it with some exertion and stood on the stone
threshold. It was a bleak, grey day: the wind sighed
through the pines and wild clouds raced across a cold
sky; gusts of wind blew dead leaves about, and a few
drops of rain fell. It was not a good day for travelling,
although Ebensburg was only a few miles away. It
would be a better day to stay home and write his books.

Long ago it would have been only a matter of a few
moments for the Prince-priest to have saddled his
horse and have dashed off over the hills. But now he
was seventy years old and a trip to Ebensburg meant
the inconvenience of getting out the old sled and having
the man-servant hitch up the horse, while he himself
bundled up in shawls and blankets against the cold
November rain or possible snow. If he did not do so,
he might be laid up with a siege of rheumatism that
would prevent his saying Mass for three or four days.
Alas, it was terrible to be old, with so much still to be
done. At this moment his children were quarreling
over politics and sinning by raillery, anger, revenge
and ill-will. He must go and see Conway; he'd be in
his newspaper office today; he must take him to task
for exasperating Michael Dan unnecessarily, since he
wasn't the man to pass it over.

A pale sun just then peeped out from a parting
cloud; it was a good omen for a better day in the later
hours. The Prince stepped back into his house, closed
the door and passed through the little hall out to the
barn.

CHAPTER TWO

A LITTLE CHILD

*F*ATHER Gallitzin picked his way through
the damp leaves that day over the path to
the barn door, where John, his shuffling
old man-servant, was working at a broken
harness.

John heard the sound of his steps, for he was a sharp
old fellow. He looked up from his work, and then slowly straightened himself as much as his curved shoulders
would permit. He was the sort of old man who doesn't
like to stop one job to start another.

"John," said Father Gallitzin, "will you put up the
sled? I'm going over to Ebensburg to see Conway."

John suddenly seemed a little more interested. "I'll
have it ready in no time, Father," he said, putting down
the straps and chains. " 'Tis too bad about Conway's
baby, isn't it Father?" he asked.

"Conway's baby!" exclaimed Father Gallitzin,
"What's the matter with the baby?"

"Sure, I thought that's what you were goin' about.
It's very sick; 'twas taken sick suddenly. Mrs. Kearney
said that Dr. Rodriguez was there all night."

"Why, that's too bad, John. Well, put up the sled and
we will go right away."

49

Father Gallitzin walked back to the chapel house to get holy water and a white stole, while he thought to himself how out of place it would be to scold William if his little son were dangerously ill. It seemed as though he could never scold William Conway, something always prevented it: either he began to see things in William's way when he explained, or the time slipped by and whatever mischief he had been up to righted itself without a chiding.

In about a half hour Father Gallitzin was on his way, seated in the famous old sled that had been his equipage, both winter and summer, ever since he had injured his leg by a fall from his horse a few years before.

It was a bumpy ride over the frozen ruts to the county Seat of Ebensburg, but at last the old sled was halted before a two story frame house set back in a grassy yard and enclosed by a white paling fence.

The prince-priest was assisted by his cane and his servant to get out of his unique vehicle. Although stiffened a little by the ride he made his way to the gate, still being helped by John to limber up, and they went up the cinder path together. By the time they reached the door Father Gallitzin was young again and he waved his cane, which was John's dismissal. John was a free man for the afternoon and he knew exactly where to go. He would have a "wee nip to warm him up" until the pastor would be ready to start home again.

Father Gallitzin knocked at Conway's door and then opened it immediately, as was his way. He never stood and waited to be admitted; he was the father of his families and why should he be knocking and waiting like a stranger at their doors? Front doors

50

were never kept locked in the daytime; the townsmen and villagers on the mountains had nothing to fear from their neighbors.

There was no one in the front room, and so the priest put his broad rimmed hat on the table and thumped with his cane on the rag-carpeted floor.

"William!" he called, "Charity Ann, where are you?"

Then he noticed that the door of the printshop adjoining was closed and that the usual whirr of the presses was absent.

Mrs. Conway at that moment came hurrying into the room; there was distress on her face and her eyes hollow with either wakefulness or weeping. She was usually pretty and young, but now she looked so fatigued one could not have guessed her age; some sorrow had dimmed all her freshness and vigor. A sudden look of relief came to her eyes when she beheld Father Gallitzin.

"Oh Father!" she exclaimed, "I'm so glad you've come. William is heartbroken; Doctor Rodriguez gives us no hope for the child, but maybe if you will only bless him... Oh, maybe he will revive and recover." Mrs. Conway raised her eyes heavenwards and clasped her hands in an attitude of supplication and prayer.

"Now Charity Ann," said Father Gallitzin, "You mustn't be leaping over the will of God with false hopes. We must be resigned to the plans of the Creator. I'm not one to bring back life to the dead or health to the dying. I'm a sinner like the rest of mankind, but I will see the baby and bless it."

Charity Ann led the way into the adjoining room, just off the kitchen. It was a plainly furnished bedroom with a big fourposter in one corner and two or three split-backed chairs placed around. A wooden cradle was near the fireplace which almost filled the opposite wall. A low many-paned window was in the other wall.

William Conway sat in a rocking chair beside the little cradle and Doctor Rodriguez was standing beside him with his hand on his drooping shoulders. The young father looked a picture of despair—all the cockiness and humor had vanished.

At the entrance of the priest and the mother, William rose to his feet, and all of them fell to their knees while Father Gallitzin blessed them. Then they gathered about the cradle where the life of the little son was slipping away. The baby was a beautiful golden haired child of half a year; ringlets covered the tiny head like a halo and long dark lashes lay upon the rose-leaf fevered cheeks. The little mouth was partly open and the breath came gaspingly.

The priest took a small prayer book from his pocket, and, putting the white stole round his neck, he read a long prayer over the baby and sprinkled it with holy water. There was a little moaning cry when a drop fell on its face—it was the only sign that it was still living. Father Gallitzin then removed his stole and turned to the grieving parents and the doctor.

"I can see," he said quietly, "that the baby will soon be among the angels and saints, and you good parents should try to rejoice, even while you grieve at its passing. Its pure soul will go back to the Creator Who made it. He designed you two good Christians to co-operate with Him in bringing it into this world. Now it goes to Him to be your intercessor—your very special "angel" before His Throne. By the grace of its Baptism it will shortly be admitted to the vision of God, and it will live forever in an ecstasy of bliss, according to the capacity given it through the merits of Our Redeemer. You are both blessed in this child. Had it been destined to live it would later have been equipped with the power of choice between good and evil. What would have been its choice? What would have been its ultimate end? Think, what will be the end of each man who must make his own choice? God will take this little one to Himself; in the midst of your sorrow you must try to rejoice."

He turned to leave and the three silent figures followed him into the front room. He took Doctor Rodriguez's hand and pressed it tightly; good Doctor Rodriguez, who often scolded him, had nothing to say: the grief of his friends had silenced him. The priest laid his left hand on the shoulder of William, and then he took Charity Ann's cold fingers in his own and looked at her steadily:

"Charity Ann", he said, "you are a brave little woman. I leave it to you to console William and to remind him of my words."

"Father Gallitzin," said William huskily, "I shall never, never forget them."

CHAPTER THREE

--SHALL LEAD THEM

OLD JOHN was waiting to help the Prince into his "grand coach." After he was settled with all the robes tucked around him, Father Gallitzin took out his breviary in order to pray. But John was inquisitive:

"How's the baby?" he asked.

"It is going to die," said Father Gallitzin, and resumed his reading.

" 'Tis too bad," said John, then he chirped to the old mare and again they bumped over the rough road back to Loretto.

*   *   *   *   *   *   *

The next day a little white coffin was borne to St. Patrick's cemetery in Ebensburg, and Father Terrence McGirr sprinkled some holy water over the grave; William Bernard Conway, Junior, the hope and idol of his father's heart was as a first snowdrop melted away by a late Autumn sun.

That week there was no "Mountaineer" published.

The presses were quiet and still, for the heart of its minstrel editor was crushed and broken.

* * * * * * *

In the little village of Summit, nine miles away, Michael Dan Magegan was making his way to the post office. Summitville was a thriving town with a fine big "Mansion House" at the intersection of the Philadelphia stage coach turnpike and the Portage Railroad. It had a number of stores, a brewery, a town hall, a Catholic church and a post office—the first one established on the Allegheny mountains.

Michael Dan lived at Summitville right across from St. Patrick's Church. He had moved there from Johnstown several years before, and while his clients in law (for Michael Dan was a lawyer) were fewer, it didn't matter much for he was too busy with politics to bother with people seeking his legal advice. Mr. Magegan was considered a good lawyer by those who liked his stormy methods. He could overwhelm almost any opposing advocate with the thunder of his loud and boisterous voice, his pounding and thumping, and the awful frown on his monstrously ugly old face, with its long semi-shaven lip, the beetling brows, and the fat and pimply snub nose. Michael Dan had long since lost his facial beauty.

"No paper," he growled to himself coming out of the post office. "Now what is that wily Conway up to? I guess he's off to Philadelphia to see his friends. They want him to set up his plant there and publish a paper in their city." Hope filled Michael Dan's heart, for he wished with all his soul that Conway would go and leave the field of these mountain towns for himself. The Whigs were having a hard time of it with a brilliant and loveable man like Conway as leader of the

Democrats. Conway was young, fine looking, elegant and dignified. His scornful, well chosen words when speaking of Michael Dan's policies had more influence than all the latter's loudest blustering, swearing and unfettered rage.

Conway *was* a "wagish" fellow, and would wave his silk hat at Michael Dan from across a street in Johnstown or Ebensburg or shake his cane at him in a mischievous way, while wearing an expansive and white-toothed smile, as if he had never said a mean word about him in his life. Then the very next day there might be a great berating in the "Mountaineer" that made Michael Dan fit to be tied.

All week Michael Dan electioneered with the help of his compatriots. Peter Levergood, Charley Snodgrass, and Richard Purse stumped the towns and villages for him. He wanted to be sent to the Legislature, but his chances were slim with all the mountain turned Democratic by that "wily little viper" of a Conway.

But the next week when Michael Dan came home from his political campaigns, he found all his mail on his office desk. He sat down in his big armchair and put his feet among the clutter on the top. He had found the "Mountaineer" on a pile of bills, advertisements, and sundry bits of uninteresting correspondence. The "Mountaineer" would have something spicy after a week of silence!

Now Michael Dan's desk faced a window that looked straight across the turnpike to the facade of St. Patrick's Church. Michael would have liked to move the desk, for looking at the church was a continual reproach to his conscience; but the fireplace to the right, and a door to the left would not permit any other place than just this for the desk. The one other side of the

room was gloomy and he couldn't afford to keep a
kerosene lamp or a candle burning all the time. And so
it happened that many times a day his conscience
pricked him for he could actually see through the plain
glass window in the front door of the church to the
red light burning before the Tabernacle.

Michael had fallen off from his former piety and it
bothered him. "Why should I be goin' to church and
me in mortal sin?" he reasoned wrongly. "I can't be
prayin' to Him with me heart full of hate against Conway, the scoundrel, the skunk, the villain, the devil, the
sneakienest Orangeman in the State of Pennsylvania.
I hope the people of Philadelphia will get more'n
enough of him."

With that he dropped his eyes from the beacon light
in the church to the pages of the paper. There was
nothing unusual on the front page, in fact it was un-
commonly dull. There were some items about the
progress on the new canal, some ordinances of the
borough of Summitville, accounts of weddings in
Johnstown; the visits of the folks of the mountain
towns here and there. Indeed it seemed as if the ver-
satile editor had collected no news of importance at all.
Michael Dan had expected a surprise of some kind:
perhaps a swaggering piece about a new paper to be
edited from the "City of Brotherly Love".

Ah, what was this bordered in black in a little corner
of the front page? Conway's own name! "William
Bernard Conway" with a border of deep mourning.
Michael Dan's heart gave an automatic great leap of
wicked relief and joy. But his conscience checked its
full expression, for he gave a sudden look over at the
chiding beacon, while his eyes turned again to the obituary notice and he shoved his glasses up on his nose the

better to read the fine print of the item. It was then that he saw the word "Junior" underneath the name of the deceased. 'Twas only a baby that was dead, only a child of six months and not his troublesome opponent at all. Michael forgot to repress the sigh of disappointment that came from his heart, and he didn't look over again at the beacon.

He turned the page of the paper to the columns of the editor, and there a poem caught his eye. It was long and in clearest black type:

"Innocence And Death."

BY

William Bernard Conway.

"Now what's this?" said Michael Dan, as he began to read:

"Ah this is death! I realize it now;
My son, thy earthly pilgrimage is o'er;
How pale thy cheek, how cold thy noble brow,
Pale, cold as marble,—never, never more
Upon this side of that dim, misty shore,
Which separates eternity from time,
Shall we rejoice my son, as heretofore;
Death sealed thy destiny without a crime,
Mysterious death! Stern, absolute, sublime."

Michael Dan took his feet from the desk and set them upon the floor. He pulled himself up straight in his chair.

"Well now," he murmured aloud, "did Conway write that? 'Tis his son that's dead, and not me, and so the tune is different. But I didn't think he could do so well." Then Michael went on with his reading:

"In death there is sublimity indeed,
When his cold grasp and innocence unite,
When the unsullied soul with countless speed
Soars to the regions of celestial light;

58

What awful splendor bursts upon the sight,
Splendor by which the angels must be awed;
When Heaven's high portals open to invite
The sinless soul returning from abroad,
To share the rich beatitude of God."

Michael Dan was overcome with conscience-stricken emotion. He ruminated on the words:

"When Heaven's high portals open to invite
The sinless soul returning from abroad."

He looked over at the flickering light in the little church across the road. "Sinless soul." His own, he thought, was stained with sin: anger, revenge, the wishing of another's death. And he had just done that a moment or two ago, when he read the obituary? He had missed saying his prayers, and hadn't paid much attention at mass on Sunday, with his mind full of politics instead. And wasn't this a bitter envy and hatred that he'd had toward his neighbor?

"Should the cold grasp of death seize me now," thought Michael, "Would Heaven's high portals open to invite me in?"

Michael Dan had had a good father and mother. He had been a good boy. He had studied his catechism, and had made an innocent holy first Communion, and had continued to live as an exceptionally good Catholic until political ambitions had taken hold of him. Then his disposition gradually changed. Politics strove in his soul to become a false god; he dreamed politics, read politics, thought politics, swore, cursed and fought for politics.

Yes, Michael Dan had changed and he knew it. Lately the change was greater. He scarcely knew his own face in the mirror any more. His soul's ambitions had changed the lines and appearance of his countenance; his heavy brows did not used to meet across his nose in that fierce scowl. His nose, ill-formed as it was, had not been red and swollen with many apoplectic rages. His mouth hadn't always turned down nor his under-lip protruded in that belligerent and spiteful way. Indeed he had once been handsome, when a different type of soul had looked out of his face. Once he had been vain of his good looks; now he was envious of the dapper elegance of William B. Conway. Michael Dan had never been the sort of man that Conway was. Michael was stock but well built, and he had had a great deal of masculine charm in his day. What he looked like now was all his own fault and he knew it.

"Sure I look like the divil any more, and I am one. 'Tis me sinful soul that makes me so ugly. I'd be out of place within the Heavenly portals. But to get on with the poem."

"This is thy glorious destiny my son,
Wherefore should I then murmur or repine?
Father in Heaven, Thy holy will be done,
I am thy creature, not my will but Thine.
Thy wisdom, power and goodness are divine
And infinite, and Thy decrees are just;
Chastise, but not in fury, me and mine,
In Thee with humble confidence we trust,
Whether in youth or age we sink into the dust."

Michael stopped again to ponder: "Ah, 'tis no wonder Father Gallitzin likes the man better than he likes me. I guess 'tis like that they converse with each other. Sure 'tis many a year since I had sentiments like them, so how could I be expressin' them when they're not there. Yes, I've seen the priest lay an affectionate hand on Conway's shoulder and call him 'mon fils'—and Conway calls him 'mon Père'; 'tis in French they talk to each other often. But 'tis not for French talking that he likes him better'n me. Maybe if I was the man

I used to be . . . ? Well, what else has he to say in his poem?"

"I am the Resurrection and the life."
Says Christ, who is the Truth, the Life, the Way,
And this belief must bear us through the strife
And stormy conflict of this little day
Of death's probation. Learned men may say,
But their philosophy is full of gloom,
When man returns again to kindred clay
He sinks to sleep eternal,—awful doom,
If this be true then hell is in the tomb."

"Hell!"—said Michael Dan as he took a furtive look across the street. "O Lord, have mercy on my wicked soul!"

" 'Tis false philosophy, or whence is this,
This longing after immortality, this love
Of friends departed,—beings that we miss,
Those who on earth have ceased to live and move?
'Tis false, my son, for we shall meet and rove
Together o'er the flowery alps of Heaven;
This is my hope which reason can't reprove;
My errors pardoned and my sins forgiven,
Without this hope my heart were desolate and riven."

"Sure I guess the man is takin' it hard. 'Twas his only son . . . and his wife is a delicate wee woman," said Michael Dan softening.

"Farewell, my son, my hopes for thee were high,
I wouldst that thou hadst lived to bear my name,
'Twas a bright vision—but it flitted by,
And thou art happy; what is earthly fame?
Let those who've heard this noisy trump proclaim,
Those who have loved its intonation best;
If thou hadst lived would glory or would shame
Have been thy portion? Doubt and darkness rest
On all our earthly hopes; Dignum et justum est."

"Ah, 'tis a beautiful and pious bit of preachin' he's done. 'Would glory or would shame have been his portion? What's me own with all me quarreling and fighting?' "

" 'Tis idle now to speculate, 'tis vain
To dream of what the future might have been,
Earth has its fleeting joys and real pain
To gild or sadden life's eventful scene,
But Heaven is a long felicity serene,
And tranquil as the Great Eternal Mind,
No heart conceives—no earthly eye hath seen
What goodness Infinite has there combined
To bless the innocent and pure of humankind."

"Shure it gets more and more beautiful; I always did think it was in him. I saw it in the man, for I'm no jackass, and it made me boil with rage—God forgive me; 'Twas the devil himself putting me up to it. Conway is a fine man, he is—in spite of him bein' a Democrat. Now if he'd take that paper to Philadelphia, he'd make those city folks sit up in wonder; They do be thinking that we're a passel o' green mountaineers. Poor Conway, I guess his heart's broken over the wee one's passing away."

There were still some more lines to the poem and Michael Dan resumed his reading:

" 'Tis vain to speculate, my partial eye
Saw every manly virtue in the germ,
Which death has blighted:—frank sincerity,
Decision stern, inflexible and firm,
Had Heaven protracted life's uncertain term,
Whose earthly tenure death so swiftly broke.
Though I concede that man is but a worm,
A man thy budding promises bespoke,
Unbending as thy native mountain oak.
A long, a last farewell. For we must part,
Thy grave is ready and thy wardrobe done;
I think I am resigned,—but still my heart
Clings,—fondly clings to thee—my son, my son!
                    November 9th, 1837."

MICHAEL DAN'S EPITAPH

Michael Dan laid the paper on his desk. He took off his spectacles and laid them on the pile of unopened mail. He pulled out his red bandana and blew his nose. He looked again over at the light swinging before the Tabernacle. He took out his big silver watch. It was two-thirty P.M. He grabbed up the spectacles and put them on hastily; he snatched his hat from the mantle-piece, pulled on his leather gloves and was out the door.

His horse was still tied to a tree, where he had forgotten it for a half hour, so engrossed had be become in his reading and meditation. Soon the frozen ruts to Ebensburg were flashing sparks from his horse's hoofs. Michael Dan was filled with a holy fire and a great emotion of human pity and love united with supernatural repentance for his sins.

In no time he stood at the outer door of the print shop of the "Cambria Mountaineer". He gave a great knock with the back of his hand and then opened the door.

The slight form of the editor, in his shirt sleeves, was bent over his desk close to the window near the door. He arose with a start and a look of astonishment came into his limpid blue eyes; then he stiffened a bit. Surely Michael Dan would not bring up that "Epitaph" now! Oh, why had he ever written it?

But it was a different Michael Dan who stood before him. It was a Michael Dan of years before, and his hand was ungloved and stretched out to him. It was a Michael Dan who was saying:

"Conway, I have read your poem. I can't tell you how sorry I am about the child, the hope of your heart. But I know that you are a brave man. They were beautiful words that you printed in your paper. And please give my sympathy to Mrs. Conway."

With that he clasped William Bernard's hand with such a grip that it seemed as if they had never been enemies. William Bernard couldn't speak; his eyes were flooded and his voice had left him. But Michael Dan saw and it was enough. He suddenly released Conway's hand and was out the door and onto his horse in a second. Again the stones were resounding on the old road. Once he turned and looked back; William was standing in the open door of the shop looking after him. He didn't turn again. Loretto was now his goal.

In less than a half hour the knocker sounded on Prince Gallitzin's log house door and a patient Michael Dan waited for its opening. There were no bolts to be drawn back for it was only half past three in the afternoon.

Father Gallitzin opened the door. He was in his cassock and a quill pen was behind his ear. He looked surprised when he saw Michael Dan; he wasn't used to frequent visits from him.

Michael Dan was overcome with a sudden fear; "Sure 'twas the divil puttin' it there ... Father," he said in a timid voice, "if it wouldn't be troublin' ye too much, would ye hear my confession?"

A beautiful light came into the Prince-priest's eyes as he drew Michael Dan into the house and closed the door.

PART IV

Little Maggie of Summitville

STORIES AND PUZZLES

*W*HAT little Maggie Conway liked best of all was to sit on a hassock at her grandmother's feet and listen to stories. It was then that Maggie could keep her thimble on her finger while she sewed carpet rags. It took longer to sew with a thimble, grandmother forgot to quit speaking, and so the stories went on and on.

Little Maggie called her grandmother "mother", because she was the only mother she had ever known, and that was the subject of a story in itself.

Little Maggie's real mother had had a very beautiful name: Unietta. Maggie wondered why they had not called her by that name also instead of plain Margaret Ann—which everybody pronounced Marget Ann or Maggie. But Marget Ann's father always called her "little Maggie" and she liked that better, although it wasn't so nice as "Unietta".

Little Maggie's father didn't come very often to "mother's house in the Allegheny Mountains where his small daughter lived with her grandmother. When he did come Maggie noticed that "mother" always seemed to be on the verge of a cross spell. She told no stories

when he was in the village or somewhere on its out-
skirts. He usually stayed with his sister Ann who was
married to a farmer and lived about three miles away
beyond the woods.

Little Maggie liked her father but "mother" didn't.
She sometimes invited him to stay for a meal, but she
talked rather snappy to him, and poked her ginger
bread under his nose quickly as if she'd like to poison
him with it or give him none at all. Maggie noticed
this when she was only four years old and she felt
sorry for her father. But he smiled and talked to Little
Maggie and never pretended to notice at all. He used
to pick her up and play with her, but grandmother
watched at such times out of the corner of her eye like
a sly fox until he put her down again.

Her father never stayed very long and his little
daughter had a lonesome spot in her small heart after
he left. There was nobody to play with and Maggie
just wandered around by herself. She didn't have a
doll or a story book; she really had no playthings, although she could see the feet of a doll sticking out of
a box on top of the tall clock in the corner in the
"room". She didn't have a ball, and as for candy, she
sometimes had a peppermint or two from the jar in
grandmother's window.

Grandmother kept a store where the peppermints
were for sale. Menfolks usually bought them. They
were jolly men who came into the little store and leaned
against the counter, and some of them had bad cases of
the hiccoughs. Maggie peeped out at them from the
"room" door that opened off the store.

Sometimes elderly ladies bought peppermints too;
they told grandmother that they were so good to settle
an upset stomach. Maggie's stomach was never upset

even when she turned somersaults on the grass in an effort to upset it, that she might get a few peppermints to settle it again. But when she stood up on her feet and laid her hand on her middle the stomach seemed to be in exactly the same place.

Maggie only got a peppermint when grandmother was in an exceptionally good humor or when one of the jolly men saw her peeping and coaxed her over to take it out of his shaking fingers. Grandmother looked cross at such times, but she didn't say anything and Maggie ate the peppermint with glee. Little Maggie didn't know that the villagers thought her grandmother was stingy and that the little boys said she had a whole barrel of pennies under the counter.

There was one time of the year that Maggie liked tremendously, and that was Christmas. Nice things came from nowhere to little Maggie. There would be papers with pictures in them, and a book with stylish ladies in great skirts and little parasols, and grandmother would let Maggie cut them out—actually cut the book to pieces! Maggie named all the ladies and placed them carefully between the pages of the big Bible in the "room". The most stylish lady she called "Miss Bella Ellsworth". She had heard that name someplace, and she thought it had a lovely sound, almost as delightful as Unietta.

One Christmas when she was about four and a half there was a beautiful little green velvet bonnet lined with pink silk for her. Maggie was dazzled. Old Kate McColgan, who lived in a big house out along the Portage Railroad, asked her if Krist Kringle had brought it.

"Krist Kringle? Who is Krist Kringle, Kate?" asked Maggie, for she had never heard of such a person.

"Why, Krist Kringle is the old fellow who brings

69

Christmas presents to good children. He comes down the chimney on Christmas night and leaves the things you wanted—that is if you were good."

"Then he must think I'm bad, Kate, because I want many things and I never get them. I want lots of pictures to look at. I want a doll like Mary Gaffney's. I want a whole poke of candy. I guess Krist Kringle doesn't think much of me."

But the Christmas that Maggie received the green velvet bonnet she knew that she had made a mistake about Krist Kringle. He must really like her very much to bring her such a beautiful stylish bonnet: green velvet lined with shirred pink silk!

Nevertheless, grandmother didn't seem pleased; Maggie noticed that she looked at the bonnet with a frown on her face and gave it a mean little jerk when she tied it under Maggie's chin in order to try it on, the Christmas morning that it had been left on the mantlepiece.

"Mother" didn't say where it had come from, but old Kate said that Krist Kringle brought it. Maggie asked "mother" if Mr. Kringle brought it, and "mother" asked impatiently: "who are you talking about child? Who is Mr. Kringle?"

"Why, mother, don't you know? Mr. Kringle brings nice things to people on Christmas."

"Oh," said grandmother, and then she was silent as if thinking. She seemed to get an idea for she said: "If Krist Kringle brought it then he has no more sense than Krist Ooner who shoots his neighbor's chickens. Where will you wear a bonnet like that, and it must have cost a pretty penny. Good woolen stockings or a pair of boots would have been more serviceable."

"U-u-m, I'd rather have the bonnet," said little Maggie.

70

The next Sunday when grandmother came home from church Maggie was sitting on the top step just outside the front door of the house with the green velvet bonnet on her head and grandmother's old faded shawl around and underneath her. The snow was banked up high on each side for grandmother had swept the steps. What was the use of having a green bonnet when there was no place to wear it and show it off?

But Maggie's keen imagination had found a way. Mr. Black, Mr. Sharbaugh, old Mrs. Peary, Peter Daugherty, and all the people coming from church saw her in the beautiful bonnet and looked admiringly at her. Some told her that she might catch cold; she showed these that she had the shawl both around and under her; but finally when grandmother came along she jerked Maggie into the house. But it didn't matter much as the whole town had already seen her in the loveliest bonnet that had ever been worn on the top of the Alleghenies.

By next winter the bonnet would be too small anyhow; Maggie was five and a half and all she had had was a gray wool hood that grandmother had knit for her.

Before the next winter old Kate repented of having told Maggie about Krist Kringle, seeing that she expected so much of the magnanimous old fellow and got so many disappointments thereby. But to discover the truth was a calamity: one could always hope and there was fun even in hoping, but when Kate said, "No, there is no such person, it's all a hoax to make the 'childer' behave themselves," Maggie's grief was far greater than when old Krist Kringle seemed very stingy.

71

She wept the greater part of Christmas day, and grandmother was very cross with Kate for having told her the story in the first place.

"I never told her that silly fable, because I knew how she'd take on when she'd find out the truth. I let her believe it after you told her. It kept her from knowing that it was that good-for-nothing father of hers who is the one who sends the things she gets."

Maggie was sitting in the store behind the counter sewing carpet rags, and she overheard "mother" making this speech to Kate.

So it was father who sent the clear toy candy, the story book and last but not least the green velvet bonnet of last Christmas! The carpet rags dropped from Maggie's hands and the thimble fell off her finger: there was no Krist Kringle, but her daddy had brought the nice things. Grandmother said he was good-for-nothing! Maggie didn't think so.

The snow fell dismally outside the window. It was a bleak sky, but behind the counter it was warm and cozy and not so lonely since Maggie had a father who brought her things at Christmas time. It was much better than having a stranger like Mr. Kringle bring them.

Grandmother never let Maggie go anywhere and she was always asking people who came to the store: "Have you seen anything of Jim McDermott? I heard he was over at McGarrity's last week." Once Maggie heard her say: "I have to watch Marget Ann when that Jim McDermott's around; he tried to steal her out of her cradle once and I don't trust him ever since."

Maggie was nearly six when she heard that remark and she pondered it deeply: her father had wanted to steal her when she was a baby. She wished he had succeeded. Where would he have taken her? Where did he live?

Maggie hadn't heard any more, for just then "mother" saw that the "room" door was open. She left the counter quickly and came over to close it. Maggie knew now that there were puzzles and mysteries about herself and her father and from that time forth her ears seemed to grow bigger and bigger.

Where did Jim McDermott live? Why didn't she live with him? She knew that Unietta, her mother was dead; but who was Roseann, Jim's wife, whom she once heard "mother" talking to Kate about? If Roseann was Jim's wife, why didn't little Maggie live with them? Was Unietta Jim's wife at one time, too? What puzzles in life! Oh, well, school would start in September and she would forget about such trouble. She could already read a little, for Brother Vincent from Loretto who came to visit "mother" had taught her. She could write her name: Maggie Conway. "Mother's" name was Maggie Conway too, "Mrs Maggie Conway." Little Maggie's father was "that good-for-nothing Jim McDermott."

Little Maggie was sorely puzzled: Mary Gaffney had a name like her father and mother, Mr. and Mrs. Gaffney. Why was she Maggie Conway and her father James McDermott? It was unsolvable for poor little Maggie, aged six, and she gave the problem up.

CHAPTER TWO

A STEP-MOTHER AND SISTERS

WHEN Maggie started to school the world became entrancingly interesting. She met other little boys and girls of the village and played with them at recess. This was something entirely new in her life. She had never played with any children of her own age; there was a fine big lot and garden in the rear of grandmother's house where she could play in safety by herself without any fear of a Jim McDermott to disturb grandmother's mind.

So recess at school was a delightful time. There was little Juliet and Rosie Storm, Jennie and Rosie Stuart, Agnes and Ellie McConnell, Mary and Ellie Condon, and Mary Gaffney and Josie Criste, and a number of boys.

Mr. Condon, Mary and Ellen's father, taught the school. He was a learned man. Grandmother said that he knew too much to have merely little village children on the long benches before him. He had been a school master in Ireland and had a degree from a great college there. But Ireland had been a sad place for a Catholic schoolmaster and he had emigrated. Now he earned a

74

living for his family by keeping a subscription school, where all day long and year in and year out he couldn't grow eloquent about Wolfe Tone, Robert Emmett or Daniel O'Connell, but had to stick to the ABC's and the multiplication table.

Well, little Maggie learned to read in no time. It was an easy game for one who already knew her letters, and in less than three months Maggie was ready for the second reader.

After Maggie started to school and had learned to read, a change began to come over "mother". She smiled a great deal and was pleasant with everybody, Maggie included. She would ask Maggie to read to her from her second reader. When Brother Vincent from Loretto came over for a visit, she called Maggie in from her weeding in the garden, or the churning on the back parch to read to Brother. She seemed so proud of Little Maggie. Maggie was now Brother Vincent's usual entertainer and he began to come more often to see mother Conway—or rather to see Maggie. He began hearing and teaching her the Catechism and he gave her thick books all about the Catholic Church; he gave her colored holy pictures with lace edges and Maggie put them in the Bible with Miss Bella Ellsworth.

It was now that grandmother began telling the stories. It seemed to make her very happy to see Maggie so eager to hear all about "mother's" first days on the Allegheny Mountains. There were stories of the days when she lived in a log cabin to which there was no door or hinges, but just big slices of logs leaned up at night to keep the bears and wildcats out.

Grandmother had been young when she first came with her husband; his name was Hugh, and he had wonderful auburn hair and blue eyes; "his complexion was white and rose, the handsomest man that ever lived." But alas, he had consumption and that was the reason why grandmother had come to the mountain from Westmoreland. There were so many pine trees on the Summit of the Alleghenies and she thought her handsome Hugh would be cured. "But," said grandmother to little Maggie, sitting on the hassock knitting, "the mountain air seemed no better than that of the Conway farm on Spruce Run in Westmoreland. Your grandfather died when he was only twenty-eight years old. Father Gallitzin used to come to see him and talked to him about Heaven in such a beautiful way that my Hugh, your grandfather, was happy to die.

"Tell me about my mother, please," begged little Maggie. "I want to hear about her. Was she one time Jim McDermott's wife?" Little Maggie was afraid to say: "my father", lest she irritate "mother" and she might stop telling stories for the time. Father never came around any more at all.

"Please tell about my mother. The other day when you sent me down to Sharbaugh's for some pears, Tommy saw me coming in the gate and he said: 'Ma, here comes Maggie Conway.' And I heard his mother say: 'Tommy, don't call her Maggie Conway, her name is Maggie McDermott.' "

"That's right," explained the grandmother. "Marget Ann, your name *is* McDermott, and you had better begin to write it that way. You never see your father here any more. You are now legally mine and he knows it's useless to try to get you, or I will have the law on him. He is married again this good while to Roseann McAfee and they have a family of girls and live at Mount Carmel in Westmoreland County."

"Oh then, I have sisters and a stepmother, just like Cinderella!" exclaimed little Maggie.

"Yes, you have, but you belong to me. They live in a terrible old place away out among the fields and woods, up hill and down dale. There is a small log church, called "Our Lady of Mount Carmel" but there is no school; you'd get no education at all. You couldn't live with your stepmother and sisters in such a place. I can't see how Roseann stands it; she was a fine lady of Blairsville and how your father ever induced her to marry him is beyond me. He has nothing but good looks to go on."

"But, mother, tell me about Unietta, my mother. Have you a picture of her?"

"No, child, I haven't, but she was like your grandfather, my Hugh, with light auburn hair, gold or red maybe you'd call it, and looked just like him. She was my youngest, and was only two when he died, July 1st, 1832. When she was a little older, she and her sister Nancy Ann and your uncle John used to take the stagecoach and go to visit their grandparents, John and Unity—Unietta was named for her grandmother—on the Conway farm at Spruce Run in Westmoreland.

"How old were Aunt Nancy and Uncle John then, mother?"

"Oh, they were each just a few years older than your mother. Well, on one of these trips Unietta met James McDermott at a party in Blairsville, the nearest town between Mount Carmel and Spruce Run at Livermore; and your uncle John met Maggie McDermott, his sister. The McDermotts had five girls: Bridget, Catherine, Anne, Mary and Maggie, and only the one boy, James Francis. They were fine looking folks, but just the opposite type from the Conways, who were fair, genteel and scholarly. The McDermotts were dark-haired, grey-eyed, red-cheeked and full of mischief, jokes and laughter. They upset hearts with their tricks, but they were not so brainy as the Conways.

"Mother, I like the McDermotts." Said little Maggie.

" 'Twould be just like you, with your black hair and grey eyes," sniffed grandmother, as she began to fold up her sewing.

"Oh, mother," said Maggie hastily, and laying a detaining little hand on her grandmother's knee, "I like the Conways too. Tell me what happened when Unietta went to visit my great-grandmother, Unity Conway.

"Well," said grandmother appeased, "sometimes their Uncle, William Bernard, Hugh's brother, would be there, and he was a great one for entertaining; he could make up poems and draw pictures and the children were wild about him. He was married to Charity Ann Kinney of McKeesport and he and Thomas Phillips, of Pittsburgh, published a paper called "The American Manufacturer."

Grandmother was getting off the track that little Maggie wanted her to follow:

"Grandmother, you were telling me about a party at Blairsville."

"I never did want your mother to marry Jim McDermott, and I guess I might as well tell you why, but I'll go on from where I left off. I never knew when the children continued to visit the farm after they were in their teens that there was another attraction: it was trips out to the McDermott farm at Mount Carmel. There would be a barn raising or a corn-husking and all the young folks from Livermore and Blairsville would go. The upshot was that your uncle John came home one day to tell me that he was going to marry Maggie McDermott."

Grandmother leaned back in her chair and let the sewing drop in her lap. If no customer came in the store it might happen that little Maggie would get the entire story of her mother's courtship and marriage in one installment.

"Well, I had no special objections to that, as Maggie was a good girl and John was old enough to get married, but I noticed that Unietta was having a time with herself, stammering and stuttering and trying to tell me something at the same time. So John spoke up and helped her: "and—and Unietta," he said, "is going to marry Maggie's brother, Jim.""

" 'What!' " I exclaimed, " 'you are going to marry that gay blade of a Jim McDermott, and go out and live on that desolate farm? You are not strong—you are exactly like your father and Nancy,' (my Nancy had died of a cold she had contracted, while going to Saint Xavier's, the convent school in Westmoreland); I told her that she couldn't stand life on a farm. It was different with John. He had his trade as a blacksmith on the new railroad and intended to live in Hollidaysburg. 'But,' said I to Unietta, 'Jim McDermott will make a farm drudge of you.' "

"But, 'twas no use," sighed grandmother, "I talked and talked but when my son John married Maggie McDermott, my daughter Unietta married her brother James Francis, your father."

Little Maggie was knitting industriously, with one ear cocked lest the store bell ring and break the wonderful spell.

"So there I was," said grandmother dolefully, "left suddenly alone. Hugh, my husband, lying over in the cemetery in Loretto; my Nancy buried in Blairsville; John in Hollidaysburg, and worst of all my Unietta carried away to that lonely farm at Mount Carmel. It just about broke my heart."

Here grandmother stopped telling the story to wipe her eyes on her apron. Little Maggie comforted her.

"Don't cry, mother," she said, putting her hand on her grandmother's knee, "you have me and I'll never leave you to go out to the farm."

Those were magic words, for grandmother's tears dried instantly, and she said that was enough for the present. Fate was with her, too, for just then the store bell tinkled.

CHAPTER THREE

MAGGIE'S PROBLEM AND GRANDMOTHER'S STORIES

*L*ITTLE Maggie's next problem was to find out how her grandmother got possession of her. Why didn't she belong to her own father, her stepmother and her sisters? She had never seen the sisters or the stepmother.

Maggie crawled around among the onions she was weeding in grandmother's garden, with her mind far away at an imaginary Mount Carmel. She fancied a farmhouse set among trees, and there was a big swing hanging from a tree—Maggie would have liked so much to have a swing—there were two little girls, her own sisters, pushing each other, and having a fine time. Grandmother had said that Roseann was a "fine lady" from Blairsville and so little Maggie's facile imagination pictured a regular "Miss Bella Ellsworth" in wide silk skirts and her hair in curls; she had a maid, or perhaps two or three of them to do the work. Oh, no, —that couldn't be, for grandmother had said that Jim McDermott would make a farm drudge of Unietta and

81

the life would kill her. Unietta had died. Did Jim kill her with hard farm work? Did she have to weed patches of onions and beans ten times the size of grandmother's little patch?

Maggie sat on the edge of the onion bed. The beds were raised like graves, and there were broad planks laid in the paths between. Maggie sat and cupped her chin in her hands; when would grandmother tell her the rest?

Mittens, the grey cat, came stepping into the garden and rubbed his tail across Maggie's nose; back and forth he caressed himself against her face and hands. She never noticed. He meowed anxiously for attention and affection and Maggie gave him none; she was absent from the onion patch. She was in Westmoreland County, meeting her little sisters.

Mittens suddenly stopped purring and meowing; he stood on his back legs and laying his left paw on Maggie's shoulder he gave her a little scratch on her hand.

"Ouch!" she screeched, "you mean cat," and gave him a good slap. He leaped over the onions and took his way to the barn by the well-worn path under the apple trees.

Maggie came back to her weeding. Today was Saturday. Sunday was a good day to get stories out of grandmother; nobody came to the store and the afternoon was usually quiet and lonely. Sometimes Brother Vincent came, or Kate McColgan brought Diddley, her fat-cheeked wild-eyed tomcat to have a fight with Mittens, which grandmother and Kate never knew about. Except for that sport, little Maggie's Sunday afternoons were empty, wasted half days.

Maggie and her grandmother had become great pals. "Mother" Conway talked to her as though she were a grown woman. They were always chattering together while tending store or working about in the house and garden. Maggie had much to tell "mother" about school, and to recite the "pieces" she spoke on Friday afternoons. She told of little Mary Gaffney who had to jump in order to reach the top scored line on the blackboard, but who was so smart in spelling that Maggie and she had a terrible time trying to spell each other down. She told about Tommy Sharbaugh, the nice little boy who always played with the girls and brought patches of silk and calico to school to trade for other pieces, just as the girls did. He had a doll at home and he made dresses for it. The boys ignored him completely, but he didn't care. He was happy to be with the girls, especially with Maggie, who was older and wiser. She thought Tommy was nicer than any girl.

"Mother" always listened to these school stories as though they were of great importance; but it seemed to Maggie that nothing could or would happen to her that would be half as interesting or exciting as her grandmother's life had been.

Grandmother told how she had come from Westmoreland County, Pa., with only fifty cents in her pocket. She had left her sick husband behind with his parents and her three children at the Conway farm at Spruce Run.

She was looking around on the mountains for a healthful place to settle, and she found a long three sided shed, which had been used and later abandoned by employees of the Philadelphia Turnpike Road to store tools in.

The turnpike was finished and the men had gone, and so Mrs. Conway, then, aged about twenty-eight or nine, had bought the property and decided to fix up the shed for a house. It was summer and warm; Mrs. Conway got strips of canvas and had them tacked up tightly over the open side of the shed. They were fastened with strips of wood in order that no wild animal could tear them down. It made a fairly good temporary home. Then she went back to Westmoreland for her husband and three children.

One morning little Mrs. Conway was sitting in front of her doorway rocking baby Unietta in the home-made cradle, when a tall stranger appeared before her.

At first she was startled but when she rose and looked into his smiling countenance, and felt his air of friendliness, she knew he was no man to be feared. He was of medium height but lithe and sinewy, and to Mrs. Conway, only five feet herself, he seemed quite a big man. His hair was blonde and curly, his eyes sparkling blue, his nose prominent and acquiline, his complexion ruddy and his teeth strong and white in his beaming smile.

Over his shoulder the stranger carried the biggest and most beautiful wild turkey Mrs. Conway had ever seen.

He laid the turkey down at her feet, doffed his battered old broad rimmed hat and boomed out in a stentorian voice: "Good morning, my new neighbor, welcome to our mountain top!"

Instantly it flashed to Mrs. Conway's mind that this was Ignatius Adams, the earliest pioneer on the Summit, whose fame as a hunter and generous hearted man had spread through all western Pennsylvania. This was the man of whom she had heard much. He had been born ten years before America declared her independence. He had fought in defense of his country in the war of 1812, and was about sixty-three years old. He had left his home in Adams County in eastern Pennsylvania and had settled on the Summit before the Philadelphia Turnpike was constructed. Mrs. Conway had heard all this, and so he seemed no stranger. She was glad to meet him.

"Good morning," she said gently, "are you Ignatius Adams that I've heard so many good things about?" She was returning his smile now from her fascinating brown eyes and even white teeth. Her curly, almost kinky, black hair, was tossed by the mountain wind and her cheeks were pink with blushes of pleasure at such kindliness in the great pioneer's manner.

"That's who I am!" he said with a tone that betokened self satisfaction, without conceit, in his own superiority. "I heard you had lately moved in, and that you have a sick husband. I thought I'd stop by and see how you are making out. Would you be needin' a little meat to tide you over till you get your bearings? I could let you have this bird here. He is a beauty. I have plenty of venison at home and don't really need him. He was a sly old bird, and I have been trying to get him for quite a while. This morning as I was coming back from a trip out towards Prince Gallitzin's place he stepped right out into my path."

Stooping down he picked up the wild turkey and stroked its beautiful bronze plumage; then he thrust it into the amazed little woman's arms. From a leather sack, which was fastened to his side, he drew forth two plump little partridges and added them to the turkey.

Mrs. Conway could hardly hold the burden, and so he took them out of her arms as she led the way into her house. He placed them on the table.

"Mr. Conway has gone into the woods to see if he could bring in a squirrel or a rabbit, but he is not a very good hunter; he should really be in bed. I guess you have heard that he is suffering from that dreadful disease, galloping consumption."

"Yes, I did hear it, Mrs. Conway, and that is why I came this way to see if I could lend a hand. Squirrels and rabbits are all right but a fine turkey like this is a heap better."

"You are a kind man, Mr. Adams, I wish there was something I could do for you," said the little lady embarrassed at having no way whatever to return such goodness and charity.

"Well you can," he answered smiling, as he took a sack from his side and began opening it.

"If you will just let me melt this tallow over your fire." He scooped out two handfuls of tallow and began putting it into a large iron cup which he had taken from his leather belt.

Mrs. Conway stirred up the fire in her brick chimney place and watched the old hunter while he melted it. She was full of wonderment. What did he intend to do with it? Was he going to pour it over the turkey as some trick way to remove feathers—or what?

When it was finally melted, she was amazed and amused to see him raise the cup to his lips and gulp down the tallow with great gusto and relish. He smacked his lips as he explained:

"A quart or two of this tallow will do me for several days when I'm hunting. One can't be carrying a lot of fancy grub about. Sometimes I take a quart or two of pinole along; but I like the tallow better. Do you know what pinole is, Mrs. Conway?"

"Oh, yes," she answered, "it is parched corn ground

between stones. My father used to eat it on his hunting trips. He said a handful of pinole with a drink of water would do quite well to appease his appetite until He could find some fish, berries or game to supplement it.

"Oh, yes, pinole's all right, but tallow is better," said Ignatius, "beef tallow or mutton tallow, according to one's taste. Now I must hurry away, for I left my Honor at home, and I mustn't be staying very long with strange ladies without 'my Honor'. He twinkled his eyes at her.

She was suddenly alarmed: "What sort of joke was this?" She was beginning to wish that her husband would suddenly arrive home.

Seeing her look of wonderment he laughed: "My wife's name is Honora. I call her 'my Honor' to tease her. She was Honora Burgoon, from the Prince's little settlement; you're a Catholic of course, Mrs. Conway?" She nodded. "I don't like to leave my Honor alone too long. I've been gone a day and a half now, down over the mountain and at Plane No. 5, looking for a place nearer to civilization to settle. It's too far out at the 'Place' as folks call my farm. I want to get a church started here on the summit and I want my 'Honor' and the children close to it. Honora is a brave little woman; she says that the howling of the wolves and the scratching of the bears on the door at night, when I'm away, scares her some, but she gathers the children around her and they say the rosary. They know the bears can't get in, and that I'll be back pretty soon. That's what Father Gallitzin told her to do, say a few prayers and go to bed in peace. My home's about two miles from here." He pointed south eastward. "It's just a clearin' in the woods. Hope you're not afraid here, Mrs. Conway."

88

"Oh, no, I'm not. Hugh, my husband is always here at night. We hear the panthers, and other strange cries and noises at night, but having a man at hand is a comfort, even if he is sick. Your Honor must indeed be brave to stay away out in the wilderness with the children."

"She always smiles a lot when I get back, and she'd like to keep me busy planting. But I've got the hunter's blood in me, and so I have to take a trip once in awhile; but I never leave her for any more than a day or so. I must be gettin' right back to her now."

He strapped on his various sacks, and hung the iron cup in its place from his belt, then taking up his great hat, he made his hostess a sweeping bow, and with a "I'll see you again, Mrs. Conway," he was off.

When Ignatius Adams left, Mrs. Conway sat down in her little rocking chair and mused to herself: "So that is Ignatius Adams, the mighty hunter, whom all this mountain has heard about; the man who is always ready to care for the poor, the sick and the lowly; whose table is always set for the hungry wayfarer. He is surely worthy of his reputation. She looked at the beautiful turkey still lying where he had placed it on her old wooden table. Wouldn't Hugh be surprised when he came in. Too bad that little John and Nancy Ann were at grandmother Unity Conway's in Westmoreland. And Hugh would be sorry that he had missed meeting the famous pioneer, whose jokes and caprices and kind acts he had heard about even in far away Westmoreland. She would tell Hugh how he had scared her a bit with that pun about leaving "his Honor" at home. Then she remembered the Indian joke that she and Hugh had heard he had played while the land about there was still full of red men. Adams, at the time, was working on the construction of the turnpike, and he was foreman of a band of men. He and his workers maneuvered to get all the guns of another band. All men at that time carried guns because of unfriendly Indians.

Ignatius had his men dress up like Indian warriors and they lay in wait for their fellow workmen. Upon their coming in sight, Ignatius, who could whoop exactly like an Indian, gave a war cry fit to startle the hardiest chieftain. The armed and disguised band rushed out upon their unarmed companions from behind rocks and trees.

So realistic was the onslaught that their leader told them to take care of themselves. They fled in all directions.

Adams seeing that his joke was turning too serious, called to the men, but the louder he called the faster they ran.

Ignatius was in great concern over the result of his practical joke. He was alarmed at the prospect of what might happen to the men penetrating the deep untracked forest; they might become lost for days, set upon by wild animals or real Indians, fall over precipices, be bitten by rattlesnakes. All imaginable horrors happening to them overpowered good-natured old Ignatius.

He called his "Indians" together, and removing their disguises they started out in search of their frightened companions. But they had fled so swiftly and so far it was hard to overtake them, and convince them that there was no danger. One of them was not found until late the next day, shuddering, cold and rain-soaked many miles away; his clothes were torn to shreds, his body bruised and scratched and the poor unarmed man in as much panic as if the whole red tribe had been in pursuit.

He and all the others forgave their jovial friend, but from that time on the old pioneer curbed his humorous tendencies and indulged no more in practical jokes. Nevertheless, he still loved to surprise and mildly shock people with a lively or salty pun.

This story of Ignatius Adams was one of grandmother Conway's favorites. She told it to all her relatives whenever she went back to Westmoreland on a visit. Maggie's grand uncle, William Bernard, has especially enjoyed the stories of the old hunter and warrior. Little Maggie had heard the story so often she could tell it herself as well as her grandmother, and on this particular day as she finished weeding the onions, she wondered if she might some day tell it to her own future children or grandchildren.

Ignatius Adams lived until Maggie was fourteen years of age. He was exactly one hundred when he died. Just as he had planned, he moved away from his "Place" in the wilderness and settled at the foot of Plane No. 5 on the Portage Railroad. He opened a coal mine, the first on the Alleghenies, and built a sawmill that furnished lumber for the settlers who were coming to work on the railroad.

When the settlement on the summit of the mountain had grown to be a village, Adams came forth and offered a plot of ground for a church and a cemetery. The first church was called Saint Patrick's, and a later one, built on the same spot, was called Saint Aloysius. Ignatius Adams rests in the cemetery adjoining, with a military marker in bronze at the head of his grave.

The old man had been a great lover of nature and said that his long life of one-hundred years was due to his outdoor existence. He rambled in the woods, admiring the trees, flowers, birds and animals. He found many springs; one in particular near his saw-mill, which he claimed had medicinal properties. People used to come and drink the water from the Ignatius spring, for the old man said the bitter taste, due to alum in it, would make them live long and hearty as he was. Others scoffed and said he diluted the water he drank with a considerably stronger beverage known to the Indian as "fire water". The scoffers won and now nobody bothers about the Ignatius spring.

Ignatius died in 1866. Grandmother Conway and little Maggie attended his funeral in St. Patrick's church, and saw him laid away on the very top of the Allegheny mountains, where he had come as its first settler.

Grandmother's stories were told in very haphazard fashion. Little Maggie would sometimes be in great eagerness to hear the conclusion of an interesting tale, when something would put it out of grandmother's mind and she would start some new story.

Maggie was in a fever of interest to know how her grandmother got possession of her, but it was a delicate subject, and young as Maggie was, she knew she would have to use what adults called "tact" in order to get the story out of her. Grandmother would likely lead off and perhaps tell the story of Jenny Lind, or about the time when Charles Dickens visited the Summit and hung over her gate admiring her garden. That was grandmother's subtle technique to avoid little Maggie's questions.

CHAPTER FOUR

GRANDMOTHER'S STORY OF JENNY LIND

*L*ITTLE Maggie McDermott had been pondering for a week how to ask her grandmother more about her family at Mount Carmel and especially how it happened that she didn't belong to her own father.

On a certain Saturday morning grandmother was baking a great batch of gingerbread; many of the neighbors would come that very afternoon and buy it. Her spruce beer was already in its bottles and under the sawdust in her little icehouse; folks would not be coming for that until late that night.

Maggie was washing the spoons, ridding up the cupboard and making herself generally useful in the big kitchen. Mittens kept close by and sniffed the aroma-filled air, but he didn't seem so eager for a bite as when grandmother was preparing fish the day before.

Maggie stooped and patted Mittens, pulled his tail, rubbed his fur right and wrong and thought deeply.

Grandmother looked at her sharply: "Stop your moonin' and teasin' that cat, Marget Ann, and wash up the pans. I'm afraid the gingerbread stuck a little.

redding

93

Guess we'll have to eat that ourselves; it doesn't often happen to my gingerbread."

"Yes," said Maggie, looking at it where it was turned over on the table. "It did stick; now if my father would only happen to come, he could help eat it up. He always liked your gingerbread, mother."

Grandmother stopped short as she was putting a fresh pan of batter in the oven:

"Now whatever put that in your head? Your father hasn't been here for almost four years; you are legally mine now; he better stay away. Roseann can bake his gingerbread for him."

"Oh, I just thought how much he used to like yours," sighed Maggie, not knowing exactly how to continue the subject. "I'd like to see him enjoying it as he used to."

"Huh," sniffed grandmother scornfully, "everybody likes my gingerbread just as well as he did. There was Jenny Lind, who stopped when I used to keep the little wayside inn, after your grandfather died; I had started it while Hugh was sick, and I got to have quite a business. Hugh had talent like his brother, William Bernard, and he printed me a sign: 'Gingerbread and Spruce beer for sale here.' It was a very nice sign; I hung it over the front door of the room there. The stagecoach would always stop and passengers would buy. Foine ladies and gintlemen would come in. I had one long table and several little ones; they seemed to like the little tables best. The way they bought up my gingerbread and drank my spruce beer was a caution!

"I had started out with fifty cents but it wasn't long till I was making a good living. But Hugh was dead by that time. Dear me! When I think of those days..."

Maggie knew that "mother" was ruminating again

94

in the past; Maggie had lost her cue to the story of how her grandmother had got possession of her.

"Yes," said "mother" Conway, "I had notables eating and drinking at my tables. I was going to tell you about Jenny Lind, the famous Swedish singer. That was about 1850. You weren't born yet. Your mother, Unietta, and Jim were living in Derry. I had made him take Unietta off that farm."

Maggie saw a chance:

"Oh, was it you, mother, who got Unietta away from Mount Carmel?"

But grandmother intended to talk about Jenny Lind; it suited her purpose better.

"Jenny Lind was a great singer," continued grandmother reminiscently, and ignoring little Maggie's anxious question. "It was P. T. Barnum, the circus man, who had her brought to this country from England. She was called the Swedish nightingale. She was a world famous singer. She stayed for two years in America."

"What brought her to the Summit, mother, if she was so famous?" asked Maggie, hopelessly giving up the subject of Mount Carmel, the McDermotts and her father.

"She was on her way to Philadelphia to sing, and she passed over the new turnpike by stagecoach. She was a lovely little lady and when she came to my inn she was delighted with everything and much impressed with the idea that she was on the summit of the Alleghenies. There was a gintleman and a lady with her, but I didn't pay much attention to them, as they too, were giving all their interest to Jenny. After they had their spruce beer and gingerbread, which Jenny said was the best she had ever tasted, she asked me where was the very highest point of the mountain. I took her to the window there and pointed up to Johnson's hill.

"It was late in the summer; maybe it was September or October, but everything was still fresh and green, for spring came late that year. Jenny said to me: 'Will our coach go over that hill?' 'Yes,' said I, 'the turnpike goes right over the top.'

" 'Oh, I'm going to sing on the highest peak,' she said, clasping her hands, as if that would be a great feat.

"She began to hum the 'Last Rose of Summer' and I would have gotten in the coach and gone along, but I couldn't leave my customers. But men who were clearing on the hill, told me that she jumped out of the coach, and while the driver waited, she ran to a little grassy mound—the spot from which you can see five counties—and she sang 'The Last Rose of Summer' to the winds, the woods and the clouds, as she said she'd do. Then she hopped back into the stagecoach and went on to Philadelphia. It was a famous concert there on that hill but nobody heard it save the clearin' men and the birds. She, who had sung in the Grand Opera at Paris, and in the Royal Swedish Academy of Music at Stockholm and in almost every great city of Europe."

"Mother, how do you know so much about her?" asked little Maggie, who was always amazed at her grandmother's knowledge of events.

"Why, I read about her. I've been subscribing for the Philadelphia Ledger for years."

"How long did Jenny stay in America?" asked Maggie, putting the batter crock in the dishpan and shoving Mittens away from her feet.

"She stayed until sometime in 1852. She was married in Boston to Otto Goldschmidt of Hamburg, who was in this country too. But she was never called anything but Jenny Lind by the people. Her real name had been Johanna Maria Lind. Her mother had kept a school for girls. She was a well-educated person". Grandmother always spoke with great esteem of educated persons.

"Mother, you know a great deal," said Maggie admiringly. "You know as much as Mr. Condon, don't you?"

"Well, I wouldn't say that, but I had to keep up with the Conways; both William Bernard and Hugh were bright boys, and their brother John, too, until he took scarlet fever and it left him deaf. I read up and taught myself, after I came from Ireland as a girl. Hugh went to School in Wilmington, Delaware, where he was born in 1804. The Conways valued education, and that's one reason why I got you. I want you to be well educated, but I'm not sending you off to Saint Xavier's, in Westmoreland, like I did my Nancy Ann. I could, but Mr. Condon is just as good a teacher as anybody. He has a degree from a great Irish College, Mr. Condon has. 'Twas at Maynorth he got it, indeed!"

Maggie was impressed, and grandmother continued, as she took the last of the gingerbread from the oven.

"Yes, that's why I got you. I wrote to your father and told him that I'd make you my heir—and that I will. But when I legally adopted you I told the lawyers that I could see to it that you were educated. Your father let me have you, but of course his principal reason was that you'd be my heir; he has an idea that I'm pretty well off."

"Oh," said Maggie, wiping the dough-tray, absently,

She had the gist of the story now, how her grandmother got possession of her. It wasn't nearly so fantastic or exciting as she expected. Lawyers (her uncle William Bernard had been a lawyer, and old Michael Dan Mays was one) had come to "mother's" house, or she had gone up to Ebensburg, the County seat, and her father had signed her over to grandmother so that she would be her heir.

*   *   *   *   *

Then Maggie remembered that when she was about six years old, grandmother had some men in the store one evening, discussing something about adoption papers. She heard "mother" say "Marget Ann"; and just as little Maggie cocked her ears, grandmother came and closed the door.

A day or so later "mother" went to Ebensburg. Aunt Maggie and her little Willie, from Spruce Run in Westmoreland came early that day for a visit. They brought deaf granduncle John with them. Aunt Maggie went over to her sister Annie's, Mrs. McGarrity, who lived on the farm beyond the woods, and left Willie and herself with the old granduncle.

Aunt Maggie was the McDermott who had married grandmother's son, and Willie was one of her little boys.

Little Willie and Maggie knew that they were going to have plenty of fun together, for granduncle John wouldn't bother about them, although they had been left in his care. It was Civil War time and they played that the nice fat cabbages in grandmother's garden were soldiers, and taking the big bread knives they ferociously slashed every one of them.

After that they chased each other all over the yard, for Willie had decided to be an Indian and to scalp

Maggie. She had run into the house and tried to hide behind the tall clock, but when she squeezed into the space: crash!—it fell on its face, its great full length downward on the floor. It looked like a mighty Southern general conquered and dead.

She and Willie had gazed at each other in consternation, but they couldn't lift the clock. Deaf granduncle John sat on a stool in the store poring over a book and never heard it fall. But, oh, when grandmother came home! That was a day little Maggie would never forget. Surely that was the time grandmother had gone to Ebensburg to adopt her, for mad as she was about the clock, Maggie heard her say to Aunt Maggie: "Well, Jim signed little Maggie over to me." Everybody had seemed glad, even though the cabbages were ruined, the glass face of the clock was shattered, and a great long piece was broken off its door. Then Aunt Maggie, and her husband, John Conway, little Willie and granduncle John Conway, left for McGarrity's farm to meet Jim McDermott and go home to Westmoreland. But before they went, Uncle John and granduncle John lifted the clock and set it back in place. In a few days Mr. Sharbaugh came and put a new glass on its face. Grandmother made sauerkraut of the ruined cabbages and everything ended in peace.

"Mother," said little Maggie timidly, "was the day I broke the clock the day you got me legally?"

"Yes," said grandmother, examining the cooling gingerbread,—"my, isn't that the nice gingerbread? That batch didn't stick a bit."

Maggie said no more, because the subject of the broken clock door always riled "mother." But she was not through asking questions about herself.

CHAPTER FIVE

"OLD OONER" AND THE LITTLE BROWN HEN

SO FOR little Maggie the problem of how her grandmother got possession of her was settled. The next question to crop up was: Why did grandmother dislike Jim McDermott, little Maggie's own father?

Maggie decided it was that he had won the heart of grandmother's beautiful daughter with the Dresden china complexion and red-gold hair and had taken her away to Mount Carmel farm. And the work had killed her—or almost—before "mother" had made Jim take her to Derry. Derry probably was a town. These things must be settled to Maggie's satisfaction, but she must go easy, and ask questions only when "mother" was in a proper humor, or she would lead off the track and tell some other story, interesting enough, but not the one Maggie had aimed to hear.

Maggie was interested in her own life as it touched that of her father. She liked him immensely; she thought him handsome and kind, pious and good, for whenever he spoke of his father, who was dead, he always said: "May the Lord have mercy on his soul." He always said "Grace" devoutly before and after meals and went to Saint Patrick's church on the Summit where Maggie saw him on Sundays with his sister Anne, who had married McGarrity and lived on the farm beyond the woods.

When Maggie saw her father at church, he always came over to her, held her hand and looked at her as if he would like to keep her with him; but grandmother was always standing right behind her and so he merely said: "Well, little Maggie," and to "mother" he said: "How are you Mrs. Conway?" She answered every time: "Right well. How's your folks?" It made no difference even if little Maggie had just recovered from the measles or the mumps.

Father might answer: "Roseann has a cold and Dot had the croup and the baby cries so much." Grandmother showed very little interest. It was grown-up talk to little Maggie and there was no use prying into it. Maybe Dot was her sister and the baby a new brother for all she knew. Roseann was her father's wife, Dot was a mystery, and the baby—whose baby— what baby...? It all went off in a haze.

But Maggie liked her father. After she was six she saw less of him. Yes, it was after that when grandmother legally owned her. Her father let her go because then she would be "mother" Conway's heir. That meant she would have this store and garden whenever grandmother died, which might be a long time from now. She didn't wish "mother" to die but she did wish for her father and for her sisters.

What puzzled Maggie more was the fact that "mother" liked Jim's sister Anne, who had married McGarrity and lived on a farm just beyond the woods. Little Maggie called her father's sister, "Aunt Anne", and she often came over to grandmother's store. She had two children, Charley and Mary, and Maggie saw them at such times and played with them.

Grandmother also liked Maggie McDermott, who had married her only son, John, who first lived at Hollidaysburg as a blacksmith on the Portage Railroad. Afterwards he went to live on the Conway farm at Spruce Run in Westmoreland. He took charge of the farm. His grandparents, John and Unity, had died and were buried in Blairsville, called "Saint's Rest". Old deaf granduncle John still lived there. They lived in the old log house that John and Unity had built when they first moved from Wilmington, Delaware, to Westmoreland, after they had come from County Fermanaugh in Ireland in 1789. That was a very long time ago!

Grandmother talked about all these things, and little Maggie liked to ponder them while she worked or sewed. But "mother didn't like to see her "moonin'" as she called it. She always gave her a running job if she saw her dreaming over her needle and thread. She would say:

"Here, Marget Ann, take this pan and go out and dig up a few potatoes for supper. Bring some onions in too on your way back. Hand me that apron you're sewing and I'll finish it. Give the chickens a handful of corn; we'll let them out for an hour before sundown, they can't do much harm in the garden then, besides you can watch them; it will keep your mind occupied."

Maggie's dreams would be shattered, her problems unsolved. Sometimes she gave them entirely up for weeks at a time and became wholly interested in other things.

One summer Maggie had a little brown hen of her own that kept her busy. It wasn't penned up; so Maggie had to keep it out of the garden. It was very tame and Maggie could pick it up in her arms, and it would come and eat out of her hand.

Late in the summer, when Maggie was about seven or eight the little hen hid her nest under the barn, for grandmother, like most of the villagers, kept one cow, and so had a barn or rather a little stable.

Grandmother didn't want any more young chickens, but Maggie loved the fuzzy little things. She didn't let on to her grandmother when she saw the hen steal under the barn day after day.

One day the hen went in and stayed a long time. When she came out she only remained long enough to get some feed and a drink of water. Maggie knew by this that she was "setting" and Maggie's heart was thrilled. She watched her little hen day after day and could hardly hold her excitement when at last one day the little hen came out from under the barn with seven little chickens following her.

Maggie could keep her secret no longer and called: "Oh, mother, come and see! Here comes my little brown hen and she has some little ones following her; and oh, here comes another, and another, and another!"

Maggie kept shouting "another" so often that the grandmother who heard her urgent cry and had come running, couldn't believe any hen, especially that little brown one could have so many "anothers."

But Maggie was right, for by the time the grandmother had reached the hen, she was surrounded with so many fluffy little yellow balls they could hardly count them. They finally got things settled enough to decide there were sixteen.

Sixteen little chicks with such a little brown hen for a mother!

Well, even though grandmother wasn't so pleased to have so many chickens late in the year, she couldn't resist Maggie's pleasure in her find and said she could have them for her very own.

Maggie fed them every day and was having the happiest time of her life, when one day on going out to take another look at her treasures, she found them all gone.

Her grandmother heard her cries of disappointment and came quickly to see what was the matter. She knew they surely could not be far away and set out with the little girl by the hand in quest of them. They looked in the hen house, the coal house, the wood house, the barn, under the barn, and all through the garden, but there was no trace of her treasures.

Suddenly they heard a distant clucking. When they went to investigate they found that it came from behind the high board fence that surrounded the back yard of their next door neighbor, "Old Krist Ooner", who was the terror of the neighborhood. He drank and swore and shot his neighbors' chickens; he never went to church; he chewed tobacco and spat anywhere. He was a tall gaunt old leathery faced fellow with a terribly wicked eye. He lived all by himself and some people said he was possessed by the devil. He never washed and he never shaved; he just cut his whiskers off with the scissors. Nearly all the villagers were afraid of him, especially the children. Men said he was more crazy than wicked, and that if he ever became sober he might not be so bad. Nobody ever went to his house. He had no buddies; he had no wife; he didn't even have a dog. But he had a gun and a big whiskey bottle.

So little Maggie saw where her little brown hen and

chickens were. She looked at her grandmother and her grandmother looked at her. Little Maggie's heart sank. No one would dare ask "Old Ooner" to return the hen. Grandmother wouldn't dare irritate the old reprobate for fear she would not be able to ever live in peace again. He had likely thrown the hen over the fence himself, and the chickens being so small followed under the fence after her.

Not knowing how to solve the problem they both went sorrowfully back to the house. Maggie was disconsolate. She grieved for her pets so much that it made her grandmother very unhappy. But she didn't know how to retrieve the hen, for the fence was so high she wouldn't crawl over it to get the little brown hen.

Maggie wasn't to be outdone. She thought and thought about her little chicks and the little mother hen. Every time she saw old Ooner go away from his house she went up along the alley that separated her grandmother's property from his and peeped through the cracks of the fence at her little fuzzy friends.

She watched the old man every day. One day she saw him going to the tavern to get whiskey. It was only a short distance down the road but Maggie knew he would be longer than usual; he would likely quarrel with the tavern keeper a bit, as he always fought with everybody.

Maggie fairly flew up the alley to the high board fence, and straining, stretching, and not even noticing the splinters she was getting in her hands and feet, for she was in her bare feet, she finally got over the fence.

Grabbing up the hen, she struggled once more until she could push her over the top. Then frightened almost to death lest old Ooner would grab her any minute she finally tumbled over the fence and was once again in the alley safe with the little brown hen.

The chickens were already starting to come out and to follow their mother.

Maggie's heart was pounding so fast she could hardly count the chickens, but at last they were all out. Maggie took to her heels and didn't stop until she landed with the hen tightly clutched in her arms and the sixteen chickens following in her grandmother's kitchen.

Grandmother was as pleased as Maggie and immediately they both built from store boxes a little pointed pen with lattice work across the front. Maggie kept her hen in it in the daytime where she could peep in at her and the chickens could run in and out at will.

Maggie set the pen on the far side of the garden where old Ooner could neither see nor hear the little brown hen and the chicks. At night they were safely locked up in the coop with the other chickens, and Maggie had the pleasure of knowing that her pets were safe until they were grown up chickens and could take care of themselves.

So sometimes weeks would pass, even months, without Maggie's bothering much about her family connections; but the subject was sure to crop up again.

CHAPTER SIX

DIVERSIONS OF LITTLE MAGGIE

*L*ITTLE Maggie McDermott was an apt pupil at school. She easily reached the head of her class in all her lessons, but she was not always serious in her classroom demeanor. One day a big biscuit that one of her little friends had brought to school rolled out on the seat; Maggie thought it would be fun to double up her fist like one does to shoot marbles, and shoot it back into the desk. But Maggie's aim was bad and the biscuit instead of going where it should, shot off the seat and up into the middle of the school room floor and landed at Mr. Condon's feet.

Now Mr. Condon was a tall stern man, with a great long upper lip, a stony face, and an assumed cold grey eye. The eye could twinkle when he was among grown folks, and Maggie had heard him tell of some of his pupils' pranks to her grandmother, therefore she didn't have implicit faith in his sternness. However, she knew that he maintained rigid discipline in his school, and corporal punishment was the rule. He had a long birch "persuader" over the top of his bookcase and it often came in handy.

Sometimes when **Mr.** Condon's pupils grew restless and whispering was heard usually in the vicinity of Maggie McDermott, Josie and Annie Criste and Mary Gaffney, this stern schoolmaster would step down from his chair on the high platform; he would take a big knife from his pocket, unsheath it from its leather case, and with the look of a pirate upon his face he would with great circling gestures begin to sharpen it upon his leather boot, keeping at the same time a glaring eye upon the culprits. He spoke not a word, but his terrible gestures told them better than any language that all their little tongues were in fearful danger. He would then sheath the knife slowly, still glaring, and put it back in his pocket.

Well, Mr. Condon now looked at the impudent biscuit and then over his glasses at Maggie. Maggie became suddenly shy and tried to smile in order to conciliate, if possible, Mr. Condon's wrath. But alas, the strict rule of discipline had to be kept, and poor little Maggie was brought up to the front of the room and given a switching. Her little heart was broken with shame, but as

she was a cheerful soul by nature, it was not long until the wicked deed and its awful punishment were forgotten.

In Mr. Condon's school nearly all the small girls wore earrings, for it was thought in those days that pierced ears made eyes keener and brighter. So one day Maggie's grandmother bought her a pair of hoop earrings. They were just plain little golden hoops but in Maggie's eyes they were the most beautiful ornaments she had ever seen, and she could hardly hasten off quickly enough to Mrs. Criste's house to have that lady pierce her ears. This she did by rubbing the lobe of Maggie's ear between her thumb and finger until the lobe was red and numb; then she took a needle and pierced a hole right through; after that a silk thread was run in the hole and Maggie was to pull it back and forth to keep the hole from growing shut. As soon as the hole was healed, the ears were ready for the earrings and Maggie could scarcely wait to see the effect. Now she would be just as stylish as Mary Gaffney, Juliette Storm or Annie and Josie Criste. She didn't mind if her hair was bobbed rather short and held off her face with a long curved back-comb, because the earrings would only show so much better.

After awhile she got used to her ornaments and she began to think how nice it would be if her cat could have earrings too. The next time she was permitted to visit the Criste children—Annie, Josie and their little brother Alfred—she took her little grey cat along —not Mittens—but Susan, a new ilttle kitten that Mrs. Johnson had given her.

When Maggie suggested earrings for Susan, to the little Cristes, they all got their heads together trying to devise something that would take the place of earrings.

While they were thinking, they noticed some bits of silk floss that Mrs. Criste had been using to trim the patches on what was called a "crazy quilt" she was making. It was called "crazy" because the patches were not cut in orderly shape or design, but just sewed together as they happened to be cut from the cloth.

Maggie, Josie and Annie pounced on these bright bits of floss and made little tassels from them. Then Maggie clutched her little cat tightly while Josie and Annie rubbed and pierced its ears just as they had seen their mother pierce Maggie's. The cat scrambled and meowed to get loose, but they were not diverted from their purpose. It had not hurt them very much to have their ears pierced, and so they decided Susan was making an unnecessary fuss, and they held on tighter. Soon the ears were pierced and the tassels tied in place; then they fairly screamed with delight and laughter, so pleased were they to see Maggie's cat running around with bright red tassels in its ears.

Little Alfred then went and caught their own cat and the girls put tassels in its ears also.

Mrs. Criste and Mrs. Conway were horrified when they saw what their children had done after their own example.

Children who lived in those long ago times on the Allegheny mountains had no ready made amusements, like movies, roller skating, automobile rides and such. They were all, therefore, pleased with the smallest diversion. Maggie had a great capacity for amusing herself, as well as amusing others. When she had some new diversion, she was perfectly happy and never gave a thought to her father and sisters far away at Mount Carmel in Westmoreland. Her grandmother was glad to see her so satisfied.

One thing that Maggie liked to do was go up to Johnson's farm. It lay on the brow of a hill about a quarter of a mile from Maggie's house. This was the hill on which Jenny Lind had sung her song to the birds and the winds. It was a beautiful hill—the very top of the Allegheny Mountains—and all the country was spread out below—east, west, north and south. On the east side was a spring—the source of the Blue Juniata River which hurried away to join the Susquehanna; on the opposite side was another spring—the source of the Conemaugh that caused the terrible Johnstown flood of 1889.

Everything was below Maggie when she stood on the brow of this hill; it seemed like a stepping-off place into heaven.

After Maggie had been legally adopted and therefore safe from Jim McDermott's stealing propensities, she was allowed to roam about over the countryside with the other children of the village. She had to have all her chores done first: the carpet rags all sewed and made into neat balls, the chickens fed, the candles made, or the weeding finished; then she could be off to visit little Sally Smiley who spent her summers at Johnson's farm.

The Johnson family lived in an old log house with a very large fireplace at one end. Over this fireplace the Johnson boys kept their guns. Maggie was always afraid of these guns; when big Jim and Charley Johnson took them down to go hunting, Maggie would run and hide under a bed. You see the lower part of the house was all one vast room and the beds were at the end farthest from the fireplace. They were large high beds and were always made up with patchwork quilts almost reaching to the floor, and that made a good place for a little girl to hide. The trundle beds of children were placed under them in the daytime; these were very low beds and they were pulled out at night.

The Johnsons were all grownups, but Sally Smiley, Mrs. Johnson's little grand daughter, would come to visit them from Philadelphia. She usually stayed all summer long. She had very nice clothes. Maggie liked to look at them.

Maggie and Sally liked to walk in the woods together in the long summertime. Sally knew almost everything that grew in the woods, for her uncles, Charley and Jim, had taught her about them. Sally had much fun teaching Maggie. Sometimes when they were walking along Sally would suddenly swoop down and start to dig in the ground; she would pull up some sort of little bulbs, which she called wild potatoes, and eat them. She would dig up sweet myrrh, also, which was almost as good as candy. It tasted like the black Easter beans that children like so much these days.

Maggie and Sally would often see the deer leaping through the woods and over the meadows below the house; they stared at them as long as they could see them; they were so pretty and graceful. Sometimes when Maggie and Sally were sitting quietly working on samplers in the big room at Johnson's, a deer would come up and put its head in the door. Sally and Maggie would keep very quiet and the deer would turn its head with the great branched horns, this way and that, towards the fireplace where the guns were resting, towards the beds at the other end, and it would never notice the two little girls. Then it would withdraw its beautiful antlers and turning dart away. Maggie and Sally would look at each other almost in rapture. Then they would continue their stitching, whispering and hoping for another vision before Mrs. Johnson with her grown sons and daughters should return from the meadows, where they usually were on summer afternoons, planting and hoeing.

Maggie did not remember ever having seen Mr. Johnson; she took it for granted that he was dead. Charley and Jim were big brawny and sinewy men with handsome lean faces. Their two grown sisters were very beautiful and had pale gold coronets of hair wound around their heads. Their younger sister Alice was Sally's mother. Mrs. Johnson was lean and gaunt; she had white soft hair showing out from under her black calico sunbonnet; this bonnet she never took off as far as Maggie knew. Her eyes were blue and kind. Maggie knew nothing more about the family but they all fascinated her. Somehow she never asked her grandmother anything about them. It was enchantment to go to Johnson's on a June day and be given a piece of bread with butter and brown sugar on it, to eat berries from the bushes and drink water from the springs, to stand with Sally on the high hill at sunset and say goodbye.

Maggie went back to her grandmother's house after a day at Johnson's with Sally, bearing a loneliness in her little heart that peppermint candy, hens and little chickens, tassels in cats ears, lace edged holy pictures and all her own amusements could not satisfy. Life at home seemed very sober and dull. It did not occur to Maggie until some time later that there was another side to the life on Johnson's farm that was not so pleasureable as the summer days with Sally.

One of the soberest and dullest jobs of Maggie's existence at her grandmother's and that she never considered might be a great part of Johnson farm life, was "snitting" apples.

Maggie hated and despised to "snit" apples. The juice of the apples soaked into your fingers and in a short time they were wrinkled and wizened and felt terrible. You couldn't put them in your mouth and suck the feeling away, for that was unsanitary for the "snits". The "snit" knife became black and awful to feel, but still you must keep on paring and snitting until the last apple in the basket was done.

Everybody in the village made "snits" in the fall when the apples were ripe. You see, the people of Maggie's time couldn't go to a store and say: "I want to buy a can of peaches, some juicy pineapple and pears." There were no canned fruits at all, and so people dried fruit and put it away for the winter.

Apples were the easiest fruit to dry. The apples were pared and quartered; they were then spread out in the open air and when they were well dried they were known as "schnitz." But nearly everybody on the mountain top said "snits" unless they happened to be genuine Germans, who of course, pronounced the word correctly. Most of the mountaineers were a mixture of German, Irish, Welsh and Scotch, with here and there some French, especially Alsatians. They were all descendants of Prince Gallitzin's early settlers whose villages had spread by Maggie's time for hundreds of miles, down over the mountain on all sides.

Prince Gallitzin had been dead nine years before Maggie was born.

Grandmother used to tell Maggie, who did not like "snit" pie, that Prince Gallitzin used to eat a piece of the snit pie that she had baked. Grandmother thought it had been a great honor to herself for the Prince to eat her pie, for he was very abstemious and mortified and hardly ate more than a bird would at any time.

Maggie quietly decided that the Prince was mortifying himself when he ate "snit" pie.

"Mother" Conway was really not a great "snitter" having only a few apple trees, but she did snit a little— or rather she set Maggie at the job. It was Mrs. Dan Criste, who pierced little girls' ears, who was the champion snitter of Summitville. Mrs. Criste dried all the apples she could get her hands on. Josie and Annie as well as all the uncles and aunts used to help Mrs. Criste do her snitting.

In the fall Mrs. Criste dried the apples everywhere she could find space for them: snits were spread out on tables in the kitchen, on tables on the porch and under the tables; they were in pans on the wood-house roof, on the spring-house roof; they were laid out on pieces of sacking in the back yard. When there was no more room to lay them out to dry, they were threaded on strings by means of darning needles and hung up on the clothes line or from the kitchen ceiling if it was raining outdoors.

When Maggie went to Cristes in the fall she was treated to snit pie for refreshments. At home she rebelled even when told of how a Prince had partaken of it, but at Cristes she sat up and ate it like a heroine.

Mrs. Criste had so many snits that sometimes it was difficult for her to find a place for them all, when the snit rush was on. One day she had some in a basket and hung on a nail above the door between her kitchen and sitting room.

Now no one in Mrs. Cristes family was very tall and so the snits were safe up there. But Mrs. Cristes husband, Daniel, who was always bringing visitors home, brought in a tall stranger one day. Before anybody had time to warn the man he started to go through the doorway. His head bumped the basket and the snits came down all over him and scattered on the floor in all directions.

Maggie, who was there, and the Criste children could hardly control their laughter, but when they caught the stern look on Mrs. Criste's face they managed to straighten their smiles and started to pick up the snits. "Mother" Conway shook with laughter when Maggie came home and told her about the snit shower.

On a bleak grey day not long after, Maggie was sent by her grandmother up to Johnson's farm to get some camomile that Mrs. Johnson had promised.

Sally Smiley had gone home long before, and Maggie had never been to Johnson's when Sally was not there.

When she knocked she was admitted by Jim Johnson with a paring knife in one hand and a pan of snits in the other. All the Johnsons were industriously snitting! Charley and some old man Maggie had never seen before had pans on their knees and were paring and cutting snits as if their lives depended on swiftness and quantity. Maggie wondered if the old man might be Mr. Johnson, whom they brought out from some hiding place in snitting season.

Maggie's eyes nearly popped out. Mrs. Criste was the champion snitter down in the village, but up here at the Johnson farm she would certainly lose that distinction! Here there were fresh snits by the million, not to speak of the sacks and sacks of snits already dried.

Mrs. Johnson rose from her snitting and came forward to Maggie, offering her an apple. She didn't ask her to sit down for all the spare seats not occupied by snitters were taken up with pans of quartered apples.

While Mrs. Johnson went to get the camomile Maggie forgot to talk, she was so busy looking at snits.

They were in barrels and boxes and bins; they were in jugs and kettles and pans; they were in sacks on the floor and under the table, and Mary and Anne, after giving Maggie a smile, continued snitting up more.

Maggie's tongue was benumbed at the sight. She scarcely smiled and she never uttered a word; she stood by the door and waited and stared. Mrs. Johnson returned and handed her the camomile. "We are going to make apple butter," she said.

"Oh," said Maggie, her wonderment subsiding, "I thought you were going to make snit pies."

Then little Maggie backed out the door while Mrs. Johnson closed it, giving Maggie a parting twinkling smile.

All the way down the hill Maggie's vivid imagination saw "snits, snits, snits." She knew then there was another side to the life at Johnson's farm on the brow of the beautiful hill, where Jenny Lind had sung, and where she and Sally Smiley had said goodbye. She decided she liked the falls, winters and springs, at grandmothers house quite well.

CHAPTER SEVEN

"JIM McDERMOTT"

*T*HE winters were long and cold on the Allegheny mountains and the second floor of Grandmother Conway's house was frigid from the first of December until the late days of April, when it began to gradually warm up. Downstairs in the big "room" it was comfortable for there was the great open fireplace.

During the long winter evenings Maggie would sit close to the chimney on a nice wooden stool that her old friend, Math Connery, had made for her. Here she would pore over her school books or read out of the huge Bible to her grandmother.

Grandmother liked the story of Judith and so did Maggie. This story was read over and over. Maggie's voice grew dramatic as she read of Judith's sneaking into the camp of the Philistines and cutting off the head of Holofernes. "Mother" Conway praised Maggie for her good reading. Her heart swelled with pride, for although Mr. Condon often set her to do the reading aloud at school, he never gave her a word of praise. Maggie knew she was a good reader if "mother" said so. She felt sure that Mr. Condon thought so too, but kept the praise to himself.

When the lessons were finished and the reading done, both Maggie and "mother" disliked to leave the warm chimney corner and go off to the cold upstairs to bed. Any excuse was better than none to remain where they were. Maggie would return in thought to the subject of her family far away over the mountains in the foothills of Westmoreland... She would search her mind for a tactful way to speak again of her father.

On a certain evening in early December she had just finished reading about Judith and Holofernes when a good idea popped into her head. "Maybe her grandmother thought that her father was easily led like Holofernes?" So little Maggie wisely started the subject:

"Holofernes was not a wise man when a woman could fool him so," said Maggie, closing the book and putting it away on the corner table. "He was not a good business person like you, to be so easily led." Maggie knew that her grandmother thought herself "right smart."

"Well," said grandmother, falling into little Maggie's trap, "many a man is led on by a beautiful face, and sometimes a maid is just as bad, and is led on by a handsome man...."

Little "Irish" Maggie read her thoughts. "I think my father is very handsome, mother. Don't you?" she said.

"Yes," said grandmother, dropping a stitch in the long, grey stocking, "handsome he was, and handsome he is, but his sisters spoiled him, they did."

"How did they do it, mother?" asked Maggie eagerly.

"Sure they'd go out in the fields and help with the crops as if they were men. He bein' the only boy, and they five girls of them, they doted on him, and made men of themselves to keep it easy for him. So he never learned to take the hard knocks, nor to provide for a wife and child. Anne had a letter from him last month; she sent it over to me. I like Anne. 'Tis on the mantel there ye'll find the letter. Ye can see in it for yerself that he's no provider at all, and has no business head on his shoulders."

Maggie leaped up from her stool and found the letter at once; she started to read aloud:

"Mount Carmel,
Westmoreland, November 6, 1861

Dear James and Anne,

I take my pen in hand to let you know that we are all well and hope these few lines will find you all the same. I got home and found everything all right. I have been very busy since.

McBride thinks I did the best the way I settled up with the old woman. I have to pay her more than I said, but I'd rather than be exposed to the law. John Conway appears to be pleased at us settling. He and Maggie were in town yesterday with the wagon. John was sending the old woman two barrels of flour. He wants to keep her in humor.

Murphys and McGuires are all well.

I am not through seeding yet. We have had the greatest rains here for years. The flood took two bridges off the Loyalhanna Creek and it is still raining today very hard.

I sent little Maggie a paper, it had pictures in it; she likes pictures.

Mrs. Connell is able to get to the porch again, but she is still not right in her senses.

I did not go to Greensburg yet, for I have never been so busy in my life as I have been since I got home. I have the threshing machine clearing up. I threshed all my wheat. I will have nearly fifty bushels. I could get through in a few days if the weather would dry up.

McBride fainted on Saturday last and was dead for half an hour before he came to. Kitty never got such a fright in her life. He was chopping a stick of wood at the door and dropped the ax and fell over on his back. He went into Blairsville the next day and got bled and he is as well as ever since.

I hope I will be able to get up to see you. If I can get up about the fifteenth I will stay one week with you. Perhaps some of those old widowers and orphans will pay me some money, when I think of them that I trusted for flour and everything I had, to never get one cent for it—it makes me feel quite bad. Sometimes they came crying for me to give it to them. Perhaps they are praying for me. I hope they are.

Annie I am a good deal afraid about my nose. I can't get it cured. I am afraid it will turn to cancer. I have a poor heart too. Sometimes when one is getting better one way there is something coming on in another way. But it is God's will and His will must be done. No more at present,

I remain your brother
James F. McDermott.

I am going to New Alexandria. I will post this letter there. Charles, you and your dad must come down some time to see Gimmy Layton."

Maggie finished reading and looked at her grandmother. That "business woman's" knitting needles were clicking out a determined rhythm and her mouth was set in a straight, tight line. She had made up her mind to let little Maggie see for herself at last exactly what James McDermott was like.

Little Maggie was sitting on her stool smiling comically and her grey eyes were sparkling. This letter gave her a chance to ask "heaps and heaps" of questions! Grandmother looked steeled for anything. Maggie was all keyed up.

"Mother," she asked, "does my father call you 'the old woman.' Why you're not old at all, at all."

"Yes," said grandmother, still knitting furiously, "he calls me that and sure I'm only about seventeen years older than himself. He's got my son, John, callin' me that, too. You see, Maggie, I set him up in store keepin' after he married my Unietta and she had taken sick on that farm at Mount Carmel. Well you can see by the letter how he made out—just gave away the merchandise, flour and sugar and tay and all, to everyone that came crying to him. 'Twas just as he says: they never paid him one cent, and most of it was my money that bought the goods. But his sisters had spoiled him and I couldn't teach him a thing. So he has to pay me back. 'Tis only right. He's beginnin' to pay but I had to scare them all, by sayin' I'd have the law on him. Sure, I never mind that at all. But ye see by the letter he's beginnin' to pay. But I don't waste any love on him, he's had too much of it in his life, and it spoiled him entirely."

"But mother," protested Maggie, "I think my daddy is a good man. He hopes the old widowers and orphans are praying for him. I'm sorry for him. He has a sore nose and a bad heart, but he says it's all God's will, and that God's will must be done. He sounds like Brother Vincent, except for calling you the old woman. I like him, mother, except for that." Little Maggie was patting the letter and rubbing it gently as if she were stroking her own father's hand.

124

"Oh, sure they all call me that. I don't mind. They call Hugh's brother 'old John'. He's still living on the farm with your uncle John."

"He was old and deaf when I knocked the clock down. But I think my father is a good man," said Maggie, returning to her favorite subject.

"Oh, 'tis a good enough man he is, but he is shiftless and lazy and lets people lead him by the nose. I guess that's why tis sore. Sure, and they'd never o' gotten it out o' me so easy. Well, now you know what I had against yer father. I hope ye are satisfied."

"Oh," sighed Maggie contentedly, "is that all you had against him? I thought maybe he had done something awfully bad."

" 'Tis bad enough to be so unprovidin'. He should have had more "git up" in him when he saw I was ready to help him out. I couldn't o' put any ambition into him even if I had set fire under his legs."

"But, mother, he has a bad heart. Maybe he isn't able to have "git up" like you." Maggie's little face was serious; she was pleading the cause of her father.

"Then 'tis a bad heart he's had all his life, even when all the girls of Westmoreland were after him. He was Pat McDermott's heir, and sure they all thought he'd make a fine match. But arrah, he had no eyes for any wan o' them after he got his on my Unietta. And throth, 'twas her that he got."

"Ah, I like him, mother," said Maggie exulting in her father's prowess among the ladies, which her practical grandmother condemned. Maggie held the letter up tight to her cheek: "I wish he'd come around some more, like when I was little. The paper he sent me was nice—and full of pictures. Josie and Annie thought it was grand. But, mother, who are McBrides?"

125

"Mrs. McBride is your Aunt Kitty, your father's sister. They have no children of their own; they keep Gimmy Layton, your cousin. His mother is dead; she was Biddy McDermott afore she married Layton. She was one of your father's sisters that spoiled him the most."

"And is Mrs. Connell out of her senses?"

"Ach, she's just a neighbor woman lives there some place. 'Tis a great lot o' gossip yer father always has to tell. The poor woman."

"My Daddy says that Murphys and McGuires are well," said Maggie looking at the letter again, "are they my relations too?"

"Yes," said grandmother, ready at last to tell all that she knew; "The Murphys are your Grandmother McDermott's people, and the McGuires are their relatives too. But sure there are so many of them at Mount Carmel and thereabout, ye couldn't shake a stick at thim all. 'Twas Jim McGuire gave the spot for the church there and his wee daughter named it. She said the Blessed Virgin herself told her the name. 'Twas always visions and dreams the passel o' them were having. But it was brains and intilligence for the Conways."

"I like the McDermotts and Murphys and McGuires," said Maggie stubbornly and still petting her father's letter.

Grandmother snapped her lips together: "Put that letter away," she said, "and poke up the fire a bit, and then get yerself ready for bed. I've got the bread to set for the morrow. Put the letter there betune the pages of the Bible. I must be giving it back to Anne. She saves them all in a sack as if treasures they were."

Maggie got up at once and tucked the beloved letter

into the bible. She was happy, oh so very happy: her father had committed no great crime at all; he had just been spoiled because he had been so loveable, and it had made him a bit shiftless and "unprovidin'". But now he was paying grandmother all that he owed her and was working hard on his farm threshing the wheat and getting his seeding done. She knew that "mother" did not really hate him at all; she just wanted to keep him stirred up and "gittin'," like she wanted everybody to be, Maggie included.

With a happy heart Maggie warmed her woolen nightgown at the fireplace; she had put it on over her underclothes. When it was good and warm she rolled it up like a muff over her hand and opening the stair door she shot up without a goodnight or a word to her grandmother, who didn't believe in demonstrations of affection, and was now pottering around with the yeast crock in the far corner.

Maggie crawled into bed; it was there she would say her prayers tonight, for it was frigid upstairs. She twisted and squirmed under the covers and got out of her underclothes, then kicked them out on the floor. In the morning, grab them she would and downstairs she would run. She unrolled the warm nightgown from over her hand, and sunk into the comforting folds of the great feather quilt. Then blessing herself and with her thoughts on her father, her prayers, and on God, she drifted asleep.

CHAPTER EIGHT

MAGGIE GROWS UP

*A*FTER little Maggie's two major problems had been solved there was nothing further to bother her mind. Grandmother had possession of her because she could get a better education under the tutelage of Mr. Condon and she was to be grandmother's heir. The second problem was dissolving because her father was now paying back what he owed grandmother for his having given away her goods to the poor who came crying to him. Maggie was contented, though to have no problems made life monotonous. She tried to invent one for herself by harboring a desire to see her Westmoreland relatives; but the first time she broached the subject of a visit, grandmother met it with a refusal.

"You can't be running off down there!" she exclaimed, exasperation in her voice, "you'd have to go on the railroad since the days of stagecoaches are past, and you've never been on a train. You couldn't go by yourself and I have this store to tend. Besides after you'd reach Blairsville, how would you get out to that forsaken Irish settlement at Mount Carmel? Do you think your father would drive a horse and buggy to Blairsville to meet you and me? Well, I hardly think so after the scare I gave him tellin' him I'd have the law on him."

After this great speech Maggie saw it was utterly hopeless to get to Mount Carmel. Only some tremendous event would be excuse enough to have anyone take her there. Maggie couldn't think of anything great enough in importance to call for a visit to Westmoreland. She might as well have asked to take a trip to County Fermanaugh in Ireland to see the land of her ancestors.

So Maggie's life flowed on in the usual way. Now she was ten years old, then eleven, twelve, thirteen, fourteen, and still going to school with Josie, Annie, Juliette, Rose and all the others. But Mary Gaffney had moved away to Altoona.

When Maggie was about sixteen she thought she'd like to be a sister in some religious order. She had heard about the Sisters of Mercy coming to Loretto in 1847, but poor little Maggie never went on such a far journey as Loretto, five miles away. What'd take her to Loretto with school and church right at home?

Sisters seemed very remote and wonderful to Maggie; she had seen them at a distance in her own church once or twice, but she had never any occasion to speak to them. So the idea of being a sister gradually faded from Maggie's mind. She kept on tending store for her grandmother in the summertime. Often her customers were city boarders from the Summit Mansion House, situated just diagonally from grandmother Conway's. This ancient hostelry was a very familiar point at one time on the transmountain route. It was the meeting place of many famous men. Lawyers and merchants from the extremities of the State made appointments at this house for discussions or for conferences regarding the markets and politics. And it was a great vacation spot for the wealthy of Philadelphia and Pittsburgh. It did a thriving business while the fine days on the mountain lasted. Maggie got to see the very latest fashions in bustles and frizzes, tucks, laces and general feminine elegance. By the time she had reached sixteen she was herself a very stylish young lady. She was small and slender, her face was oval and her complexion was the typical Irish white and rose. Her eyes were extremely lustrous, and a pair of arching black brows added a distinctive mark to her face. She looked just the opposite from a rustic mountaineer. There wasn't a city lady at the Mansion House equal to Maggie for charm and vivacity—neither was there one whose clothes looked any more stylish.

Maggie had an artistic eye, and she could copy and embellish any gown she saw. The material might not be so expensive, but the effect was surpassing on Maggie: a real rose instead of a velvet one in Maggie's black hair; white lawn instead of white silk; trimming of black or brown velvet instead of an entire gown of that material; real amber beads from an old Irish necklace that was supposed to be worn to cure sore throat and for no other purpose; a bit of Irish lace or a touch of grey fur; even a dyed feather from a white rooster, and Maggie was attired as the gayest of Pittsburgh or Philadelphia's most wealthy matron or maiden. Of course, Josie, Annie, Juliette, Rose, Mary and Ellen did likewise. So there was nothing rustic looking about the girls of the mountain.

But the long winters, when the "city boarders" were gone, had to be filled with something more than school, for they all continued going to school to Mr. Condon until they were seventeen or eighteen years of age.

Some only stopped when they married. Mr. Condon's fund of knowledge never gave out. The highest book was called the Sixth Reader, but the book had not the slightest appearance of a Sixth Reader of today. The print was smaller than modern newspaper type and all the stories were long selections from classic literature. Declamation was part of the reading course, and gestures fitting the subject must never be omitted. The tone of voice must also be suited to the selection, and no one ever read a stirring poem, for instance like Lochinvar, without getting all aroused and keyed up, so that the hearer could actually visualize the bold knight. There were no moving pictures in those days and so the reader must make his audience see Lochinvar carrying off his lady love and hear the stormy pursuit of her relatives to catch him.

Maggie loved this sort of thing and became quite proficient in declamation. So successful did she become that a lady "city boarder" hearing her recite was thrilled at her voice and manners and asked "Mother" Conway if she couldn't adopt her and have her educated for the stage. "Mother" Conway was horrified. The stage! Maggie on the stage! The theatre! A straight route to hell!

Maggie was sad, for to her it would have been a straight route off the mountain top and far away into a wonderful world of music, song, fine clothes, elegant people, cultivated speaking voices, and charm. She would have become just like the "city boarders." She would be something like Jenny Lind, Charles Dickens, or George Storm, the artist from Philadelphia, who sat around on the mountain and made landscapes. She would be famous, as well as gay and idle in luxurious happiness. But grandmother spoiled that dream also,

131

and Maggie felt even more frustrated than when she wanted to visit her relatives in Westmoreland.

But little Maggie had a very adaptable and naturally happy disposition. When pressed down in one thing she popped up in something else. So when grandmother set her foot down against the stage Maggie had a new idea and the village young folks founded their own dramatic club. They started to give entertainments in the great dining room of the Summit Mansion House. Criste's was the only family on the summit who had a big square piano. The Mansion House of course had its own; so Criste's was the place for practice. Josie played while both she and Annie sang; they had gentle soprano voices suited to many of Stephen Foster's songs which at that time were very popular. They had not yet become American tradition or famous. Maggie sang contralto and had a big voice for such a little person. She always made a great hit when she sang "Oh Susannah". She was called back over and over in her humorous selections. She always dressed to suit the part.

The audience for these entertainments consisted of the villagers: the parish priest, the undertaker, the keeper of the brewery, the shoemaker, the blacksmith, the postmaster, the ticket agent and others, with their wives and children. Maggie grew to have quite a reputation as the village "actress" and it became known that Grandmother Conway had frustrated Maggie's opportunity to become a real one. The subject was discussed in kitchens and general stores. Some were with "old lady Conway" and some were against her.

Maggie was about seventeen when she began to permanently take care of the altar in Saint Aloysius Church which replaced the old St. Patrick's of 1838. It had been the custom of the young folks to gather together on great feasts or for Forty Hours and decorate the altar. Christmas was a very special time that they all enjoyed.

St. Aloysius church had a very wide nave with no pillars holding up the roof and barring the view of the main altar. In this wide center aisle the young folks would build three arches at equal distances; they would cover them with evergreens which could be gathered freely in the mountain forests. There were no wardens in those days, or laws, restricting the use of beautiful wild growths: spruce, rhododendron or trailing arbutus.

After the arches were covered, tall candles were inserted into candle holders. This decorative illumination added to the candles in the reflectors on the walls. The church was almost as light as present day electricity can make it. The sanctuary walls were festooned with a great wreath of spruce made by Maggie and Tom Sharbaugh who was her devoted companion in all church work. The Christmas altar was a blaze of lights and evergreens. The young folks then talked together of the first Christmas on the Alleghenies and Prince Gallitzin's glorious High Mass in Loretto. Each would compete in telling how much they had learned about the event. The Prince had set the pace that Christmas night in 1799 and the grandmothers and grandfathers would never cease talking about it. So Christmas was the greatest festival of all in every parish on the mountain top. It was anticipated in all its Christian significance. The idea of gifts or of commercializing it never entered the minds of the people. Gifts were only secondary to Christmas confession and Communion and the grand High Mass at midnight or dawn, with brass bands and fiddles and the choir doing its loudest and best. The old folks wiped away a tear and thought of Father Gallitzin.

Maggie always went early to Mass on Sundays; she had to see that everything in the sanctuary was in "apple-pie order". One Sunday when she came back to her pew she noticed a family of boys and a girl with their parents in the front pew of the church. They had not always been parishioners. Later she saw them coming in a double buggy or sleigh, sometimes on foot. The father was a tall, good-looking gentleman and the mother small and shy and dressed very old fashioned. Maggie had seen the man on rare occasions years before at the church, but she was only a little girl and took him for a guest at the Summit Mansion House. He had looked like one of them then, for he had been very stylish and wore a high silk hat, his clothes were of the latest cut and best material and he carried a gold-headed cane.

But now this same man looked poor; his great coat was greenish and his trousers were baggy and threadbare; the little wife was dowdy; the boys were nondescript and the girl was plain, rosy-cheeked and rustic looking.

Before very long Maggie found out that the name of the family was Gracer. That meant nothing, for Father Gallitzin's settlement was full of families by that name; they had probably moved over from Loretto. But one day the father stopped at grandmother's store. He made hickory brooms and he wanted to sell Mrs. Conway some. He had one of the brooms along to show her how well he could make them. The broom was made of a piece of hickory shaved down into splints, but leaving about a depth of three or four inches not shaved; into this portion a long handle was inserted. Grandmother ordered a dozen of these good and serviceable brooms for her customers. Mr. Gracer then sat down and told about himself. Maggie and "Mother" were much interested.

The man, whose first name was Adam, had no full brothers at all, just two half brothers, who were far away. He had lately moved up from the eastern side of the mountain where he had been living at a place called Harmers Bottom. Before the Civil War he had been president of a big brick factory at Bedford. Then he had been drafted, but because of his family and to please his shy little wife, he had paid a man to take his place. He was German, but an American citizen; his little wife was Irish. Her brother, John Flynn, had lost a leg at Gettysburg; two other brothers, Charles and Will, had died of starvation while captives in a southern prison.

It had taken a great part of the poor man's earnings to pay his substitute and then the brick works had been discontinued. His partner, Joseph Soissons, had moved away to a place called Connellsville or Uniontown in Westmoreland. He had wanted to go along, but the "little woman" was so backward and fearful, and the war had done so much damage in her family, she resisted all his pleading.

"So now I have become a poor man, Mrs. Conway; but I guess its all for the best, its all for the best."

"Have you no way of making your living except selling these brooms?" asked grandmother.

"Well, I work in the coal mines in the winter and I do some farming in the summer. The boys are getting to be a help. Tommy is in the mines now."

"Tommy!" exclaimed Maggie, who had been silent until then. "Why Tommy is only a little boy; I see him in Tom Sharbaugh's catechism class."

"Tommy is ten, and an industrious little fellow," said his father proudly.

"But when do your boys go to school?" persisted Maggie.

"Oh, they get there a few months in a year; after they are big enough to work, I hear their lessons sometimes." He rose to go.

"I'll send the brooms over with Tommy or Jimmy," he said as he went out.

Maggie thought it was a poor life and was glad she didn't have to live it. But the family was of no particular interest to her. Tommy nearly always brought the brooms after that. He was a pretty little fellow, and Maggie would give him a pat on the head as she took the brooms. She would tell him how much he looked like his father. Grandmother Conway would rattle around in her old money box, and give him his sum for the brooms. "Good-bye and thank you, Ma'am" was all Tommy ever said.

Maggie's life was running on smoothly. Her wild ambitions seemed to have gone to sleep. Aunt Anne had brought over a letter saying that Maggie's father was not well and that he had moved away from Mount Carmel and was keeping a store in Blairsville. Maggie had not seen him for years and years. He sometimes visited Aunt Anne but something always prevented Maggie from going to see him. Maggie conquered the temptation to think that grandmother invented the circumstance. But it was really true that grandmother was so fond of Maggie that any thought of losing her was like a dreadful nightmare.

CHAPTER NINE

"A HUSKING BEE"

*O*NE evening in late October Aunt Anne came up to Grandmother Conwey's house bringing her daughter Mary along. They stayed until after supper. When they were leaving Aunt Anne casually remarked: (she had to pretend to grandmother that it was nothing unusual) "We are having a little husking tomorrow evening. Wouldn't you like to come down, Maggie? I'll send Charley out for you."

"Oh, yes," said grandmother, who always answered Maggie's invitations, "she may go if she wants to."

Aunt Anne gave a sly wink to Maggie who returned it with a knowing smile, not seen by grandmother. There was somebody of importance going to be there. Maggie wondered who it could be. Maybe a relative from Westmoreland!

Grandmother did not want Maggie to know her relatives; she might get too fond of her sisters and cousins and be running off to live with them, and leave her old doting grandmother all alone. Her stepmother had once said to her father and Aunt Anne had told it: "You've got a fine big daughter up there in the mountains. A 'husky mountaineer' would be just the thing to help here on this farm." Aunt Anne had thought

137

the "husky mountaineer" remark would amuse grand-mother, but she had only set her thin lips and looked ferocious.

Maggie spent the next afternoon getting ready for the husking. She arranged her jet black hair in curls around her face, and her great heavy braids she twined in a coronet behind the curls. She brushed and pressed her black polonaise. Her best dress was a black one, because that was considered more serviceable. She washed and ironed her lace fichu that looked like the Widow Todd's, who had lately come from Washington and whose style of dressing was the pattern for all the girls of the village. She then fluffed up all the ribbons and flowers on her black lace hat. The hat she had made herself, even fashioning the frame from wire. The roses on it were tiny pink blush ones that Maggie also had made of starched lawn, dyed and shaded with crimson ink. Maggie loved that hat: it was her master-piece of art and ingenuity.

Grandmother watched curiously and wondered why Maggie was taking so many pains. But she said noth-ing. Let her enjoy herself for once.

Maggie had been to huskings at the McGarrity farm before; they had always been pleasant affairs, and so she was delighted with this invitation. Besides Aunt Anne's wink told her it was to be something special. She was full of bubbling enthusiasm. Charley McGar-rity would walk Maggie home after it or she might stay all night with Aunt Anne. To grandmother it was just an ordinary occurrence.

But Aunt Anne had had a letter from her brother who was to come the next day to pay them an extended visit and bring his family along. They had never been to the mountains. Aunt Anne thought this would be a good opportunity for Maggie to meet her stepmother and see her four little half-sisters and her beloved father.

When Maggie was finally ready she did not know what a beautiful picture she made, for she had no long pier glass in which to view herself from top to toe. She was astonishingly pretty. No young lady from Blairsville could find a rustic hayseed on her.

When she presented herself to her grandmother for a final inspection, the old lady's eyes glistened with pride and she said: "My, you are quite a lady coming out of a country store. Yes you'll do," she added changing her tone to indifference. She mustn't make Marget Ann vain. "Here comes Charley." And grandmother went to the door to meet him, giving Maggie no more notice at all. It had always spited grandmother that Maggie didn't look a bit like Unietta.

Maggie gathered up a batch of gingerbread, wrapped it in a clean towel and placed it in a basket. It was to be her contribution at the husking feast. Then she started off with Charley, after grandmother had told him that Maggie could stay a few days if he would walk back with her.

They hurried down the old dusty turnpike; Charley with the basket and Maggie managing her skirts. They turned out the old Dawson Mill road. Neither said a word about who was to be there. Charley was a taciturn fellow by nature, and so he merely talked a bit about farming, the weather and the crops, and then relapsed into silence. He was not Maggie's sort at all but she was glad of the long silent spaces. She always got great joy out of anticipation no matter what the outcome would be. Maggie thrived on hope.

They weren't long in reaching the lane that led to

Aunt Anne's house. They now slackened their pace and went leisurely down the lane. Maggie noticed, while Charley plodded on, how plentiful the bright red apples were on the trees, how thick the goldenrod by the wayside, and how beautiful the blue gentians in the old rail fence corners.

At length they came to the little knoll above the house and Maggie saw Aunt Anne, tall and straight, standing out in the yard looking up as if she had been watching to see if Charley would really be allowed to bring her.

Maggie quickened her steps, forgetting all about her silent but agreeable companion. Soon she was in the grassy yard among the late phlox, marigolds and asters.

At a nod from Maggie, Charley took the basket to the barn and left his mother and Maggie to fuss over each other as if they hadn't been together for years. Then Anne hurried Maggie into the house.

When she stepped into the old farm kitchen she couldn't see very well at first. It was evening and in coming down the lane she had been facing the setting sun; but she soon noticed a man sitting at a table near the wall. At Maggie's approach he slowly rose from his chair and stood regarding her as if he couldn't realize whom he was really looking upon. Aunt Anne seeing his surprise, said: "I guess you know who it is, James?"

With his eyes still on Maggie, he slowly answered: "I think I do. You've sprung a surprise on me."

Aunt Anne was thrilled with what she had done and the way she had staged it. She stood by to enjoy her little play.

140

On seeing her father Maggie was just as surprised as he was. She had thought of cousins, maybe even her sisters, but she had long ago resigned herself to never getting acquainted with her father, or of knowing if he cared for her at all. She had kept a vision of this man so long in her mind that she couldn't help knowing who it was now gazing down upon her. He had seemed tall to her when she was a tiny girl, and now she saw again that he was a very tall man. His hair was black, his cheeks pink and his eyes clear, grey and steady. He was handsome, and Maggie knew at once why his sisters had idolized him.

He took her by the hand and kept gazing as if his eyes could not get tired seeing the daughter whom he had longed for for so many years. She could read approval in his glance, but didn't know what to think when with a note of regret he slowly and quietly said: "You don't look like your mother."

Maggie saw her father's eyes assume almost the same look as her grandmother's had, when she had once upon a time said those very words. She had done her best and her father was disappointed after all. Poor little Maggie couldn't know that her father's faraway eyes were envisioning that auburn-haired girl, dressed so charmingly in shimmering Delft blue silk, with billowing hoop skirt and flowers in her hair, who stood at his side a wife for such a short space of time.

He had seen Maggie when she was small but he seemed to have held to a false hope that she would grow to be somewhat like her mother. Now he beheld a dainty feminine replica of himself. He saw the turn of his own youthful head on slender girlish shoulders. But her figure was a trim little bit of human mechanism, just what the "old vixen" grandmother had been, not so many years before.

Alas, here was Maggie, a singularly beautiful mixture of his old enemy and himself! O'Brien and McDermott with not a speck of Unietta Conway visible. He took it all in—the "old woman" and himself as plain as day! The old woman's figure topped with his own head; "the 'old vixen' and me in one piece of perfection," he thought.

He was glad that Maggie happened to come while Roseanne and the children were out in the barn getting ready for the husking feast. He could look lovingly on Maggie with a frank and open admiration that the stepmother might not understand. He loved the children of his second marriage, but he had always kept a special and longing affection for the little girl who was the culmination of his romance with his beautiful Unietta of Prince Gallitzin's mountain.

While they were standing, the door opened and the other children began to come in followed by their mother. Maggie's father introduced his wife to her stepdaughter, whom she had always had such a curiosity to see. The stepmother acknowledged the introduction by bowing and smiling a little, but she said nothing, and took a chair in a corner near the fireplace. But she kept looking from time to time when it was safe to do so without being seen by her stepdaughter. She didn't know what to think of this radiant young creature. She had expected a buxom rustic in ill-fitting mountain clothes—and *this* was her husband's daughter!

James saw at once by the sidelong glances that it wouldn't do to make much fuss over Maggie. Yes, it was better that she had been reared on the mountains.

The old woman was right; bad cess to her, she always was. Maggie was educated, charming, refined and love- ly. Well, hadn't Unietta been so also? The old lady knew how to make them. And Maggie looked happy. Grandmother Conway had been his friend. What would Maggie have been with Roseanne?

All this went through his mind while the little sis- ters clustered around Maggie. They were glad to see their older sister who lived on the mountain. They were ready at once to accept her as one of themselves. They were not old enough to be critical, and they were glad that she was so nice and pleasant and pretty. That is as far as their little minds went.

Maggie was so surprised and happy at the turn of affairs that she had hardly any thoughts at all. She had a jumble of emotions instead. This was a moment she had dreamed of for years. And it was even better than her dream: herself in the midst of her family, and these were her own lovely little sisters. They were nice looking girls, like their mother, except Mary, the second, who looked decidedly like her father. There were Rose and Mary, whom they called Dot, next came Elizabeth and the youngest, only three, was Cecelia.

The stepmother was a handsome lady, but she didn't relax her dignity. Her sweet smile to Maggie, while courteous, was a bit cool. Maggie's Irish intuitiveness felt the lack of warm welcome. At once her mind leaped to the idea that perhaps her stepmother thought this was to be her initiation into her own father's heart and home. Independence arose in Maggie's warm little soul.

Just then Aunt Anne suggested that they all go to the barn. Maggie decided right then and there that she would stay no longer than overnight, and not even that, if Charley would offer to see her home.

The young folks were gathering and soon everybody was sitting around in the clean hay and straw "husking for dear life", laughing and chatting and looking for red ears. When one was found there was a great scampering about, either to avoid a kiss or to kiss someone.

Maggie had wanted to sit by her father, but Dan Slattery, an admiring swain, pushed himself in and she did not dare offend him. Slatterys were Aunt Anne's next farm neighbors.

But Aunt Anne's careful eye was watching and after awhile she brought her brother again to Maggie's side: "Here, James," she said, "is a place beside Maggie, I want you two to have a bit of a talk."

Her father looked delighted as he sat down on a pile of hay, and Dan on the other side looked like a thundercloud; "Who was this big stranger coming after Maggie?" She's the hardest little girl to get I ever saw," he muttered under his breath. But just then the fiddles struck up on the threshing floor stand. All the young folks dropped the corn for a dance, and as Maggie had promised Dan she was whisked away by him.

"Who's that fellow?" asked Dan.

"He's my father," answered Maggie proudly.

"Your father! Your father!" said the amazed Dan, "Is that what your father looks like?"

Maggie didn't answer, for Jim Stuart's big lusty voice was already calling out the dances and the fiddles were beginning the "Lancers".

After that she only saw her father at distances. He didn't dance, "because his heart is bad," said Aunt Anne. Maggie thought of how her grandmother would

144

scoff at that. All evening long, however, they sent smiles across the ears of corn, the haystacks and admiring swains' shoulders, to each other. Maggie was very happy. Her handsome father loved her.

But Maggie was pestered with beaux all evening. Grandmother would have been in a panic!

When the party was over and the young fellows and girls were pairing off or gathering in groups to go home, aunt Anne slipped up to Maggie.

"We've plenty of room—I want you to stay," she said.

Little Maggie had already decided what her reply would be. Her father was hers even if it must be at a distance in this world. They had had no chance for conversation, but nevertheless, they had filled up all those silent past years in a way that both Maggie and her father understood. Her father was hers, and she knew it by the smiles in his eyes, and she was his in a place where no stepmother would ever intrude, nor distance divide. It was in the world of the spirit that he belonged to her. If she were to be with him in the material world, there would be a stepmother watching, shrewd, courteous and queenly but coldly aloof. Westmoreland would no more be the dream of her heart, her home was the mountain, and here she would stay.

When Aunt Anne could not move her in her determination, she began to understand and pressed her no more. She called to her brother and while Maggie stood with Charley ready to be escorted home through the harvest moonlight, her father took her hand and bending he kissed her on the cheek. "Good-bye, my little girl," he said, "I hope that I may see you soon again."

Maggie looked up at him, her eyes sparkling: "I'll ask Aunt Anne to let me know somehow, when you are here, and I shall come. Good-bye, and I am so glad we know each other at last." He held her hand tightly in his and then slowly released it. Maggie felt the tears coming, so she hurried away.

All the way home in the moonlight she trotted along holding to Charley's arm. He had nothing to say and Maggie was busy with thoughts. Oh, to see him again! To see him again!

But a few weeks later Aunt Anne brought the word to grandmother's house that Maggie's father had died after a brief day or so of illness. He had been a sick man even at the time Maggie had met him, though he looked the picture of health.

"Arrah, his heart was bad," said poor Aunt Anne. But Grandmother Conway said nothing at all. "His heart had always been bad," thought she.

Grandmother knew that the magnet drawing little Maggie to her native Westmoreland was no longer alive; and so when Aunt Anne proposed taking her to the funeral, grandmother had no objections at all.

So dressed in one of Aunt Anne's black shawls and long crepe veils, Little Maggie stood *at last* on old Mount Carmel, and there by the little log church of Our Lady in Westmoreland she saw her beloved father laid away next to his own father, Patrick McDermott, of County Fermanaugh, Ireland.

CHAPTER TEN

"MAGGIE'S VOCATION"

*G*RANDMOTHER Conway was at last very contented about Marget Ann. Not that she had been wickedly pleased when James McDermott had died at the comparatively early age of fifty-three, but she was happy to be paid what he owed her. She was convinced of his honesty; she began to feel kindly towards him. She said to Aunt Anne: "He was a sincere good man and a real Christian." So much from the old lady pleased poor Mrs. McGarrity immensely, and she repeated it to all the relatives in Westmoreland.

Now that the real tie was broken, grandmother let Aunt Anne take Marget Ann from time to time to visit her relatives. She visited Livermore; and the old Conway farm on Spruce Run; but she never spent any more than a few hours at a time with her stepmother and her sisters in Blairsville.

For the following nine years Maggie lived quietly and peacefully on the mountain. But life was not without joy for she had resources within herself for happiness. She was a great reader. She found the old paperbound set of Dicken's works, which her grandmother had bought after Mr. Dickens had admired her garden, and although the print was very small, she read every one of them. She read them to grandmother sometimes, who was much interested in the description of Mr. Dickens' trip over the Alleghenies in the canal boat.

"Now will ye be readin' that again, Marget", grandmother would say, relapsing into Irish brogue as she sometimes did; "read what he says about ingines acomin' over the hills. Sure, 'twas like that whin Hugh and me came here."

Then Maggie would read:

"On Sunday morning we arrived at the foot of the mountain, which is crossed by railroad. There are ten inclined planes: five ascending and five descending; the carriages are dragged up the former and let slowly down the latter by means of stationary engines; the comparatively level spaces between being traversed sometimes by horse and sometimes by engine power, as the case demands. Occasionally the rails are laid upon the extreme verge of a giddy precipice; and looking from the carriage window the traveler gazes sheer down, without a stone or scrap of fence between, into the mountain depths below."

"Now where was that 'mother'? I don't remember seeing any place so steep as that."

"Arrah, thin maybe 'twas down by Bedford, or somewhere near Father Gallitzin's spring. 'Tis pretty steep down there. Or maybe Mr. Dickens was just exaggeratin' a little to make thim English sit up and take notice to the grandeur of America that he'd seen. But he tells about the planes and the ingines just right; I couldn't o' done it better meself, me that often rode over them. But go on with the readin' Marget Ann." Maggie would continue until Dickens had reached Pittsburgh and then she'd discovered that her grandmother was asleep. The book was laid aside for some other story that Maggie read to herself.

Maggie spent so much time reading that "mother" often complained that she never did anything else. But that was only her way of keeping Maggie stirred up. She was afraid that she might become easy going like the McDermotts.

But Maggie taught catechism, worked at church picnics, and tended the altar. Her old schoolmates began to marry one by one. First it was Josie to the handsome Irish ticket agent from Pittsburgh. Then Rose Storm married Mr. George, a lawyer; Juliette had secured a handsome stranger from way down East. The Widow Todd was going with a man named Rattigan; the ones who were not married were about to be; all except Maggie. Tom Sharbaugh was still her devoted helper at the church, but it was not a love affair, even though their friends did try to make it appear that way. Maggie had refused a young farmer because she had accidentally heard him swearing at his horses while he was ploughing. Maggie was very devout. She still sometimes thought of being a nun, but grandmother kept her busy in the store and garden or with anything she could to keep her near herself.

Maggie realized how much her grandmother loved her, and so it was a sad and lonely day for her when one cold January morning she came home from Mass to find the old lady taking her last long sleep in her rocking chair by the fireplace. Maggie had her buried in Prince Gallitzin's cemetery; for, although she belonged to Saint Aloysius parish, she had made provision to be buried beside her Hugh. It was there that Father Gallagher had buried Unietta. There she would be also. So over the snowy roads to Loretto the little funeral cortege had gone, and grandmother Conway was placed in her seventy-ninth year beside her youthful husband of twenty-eight and her daughter Unietta of twenty-two. Maggie stood with Uncle John, grandmother's son.

After this Maggie spent much of her time with Aunt Anne, Charley and Mary. These two cousins became to her like brother and sister. She gave up storekeeping. Her grandmother had not left her poor, but she was not very wealthy either.

Her mind turned again to many things while the years sped on. She was always out on errands of mercy: Here it was a poor old dying man, Jimmy Mahaffey, who told her where he had his gold buried. He had no heirs and Maggie had to show the spot to the state authorities, and watched while they dug it up. Again it would be a sick child and Maggie would practice her grandmother's methods and bring the child back to health without the service of a doctor. People began to look up to her as somebody distinguished and different. She seemed to get no older and those whom she considered children a few years before caught up to her in appearance of age.

Tommy and Jimmy Gracer were no longer eligible for pats on the head and patronizing smiles; they were stylish young men; they were marriageable bachelors. One of their brothers had died. He was only sixteen and an altar boy. Maggie and Tom Sharbaugh draped the altar in black for the Requiem of the saintly youth, little John Gracer.

In the winter sleighing parties were popular. Crowds of young folks would meet in the reception room of the Summit Mansion House; from this point they would start out to Hollidaysburg or to Huntingdon, down over the mountain. Here they would stop at a hotel for a good time of music, song and dance.

Maggie was always invited, for she was an asset to the general entertainment. But it seemed to Josie, Annie and Juliette that their interesting little friend was withholding a secret from them. They tried to extract it by teasing her about several young men, but Maggie would only smile evasively. Imagine their surprise one Sunday morning in late December, when they sat back in their pews at church for the regular Sunday Gospel and sermon, to hear their pastor, Father Davin, make the following announcement: "The banns of marriage are published for the first time between Margaret Anne McDermott and Thomas W. Gracer, both of this parish. Tommy, who used to bring brooms to grandmother's store!

Josie turned her head a bit and caught the amazed eyes of Juliette. The old pews began to creak and crack, for there was a stir throughout the congregation; somebody coughed, several cleared their throats and the old brewer said out loud: "Vell, vell." Maggie was in her pew in front of them all, sitting up pertly, with her little pointed chin lifted towards Father Davin's pulpit.

Mary and Ellen Condon had known the secret all the time; Ellen was to be Maggie's bridesmaid. On the twentieth of January 1885, Maggie and Tommy were married. All the old highlanders trudged to the church to see "Grandmother Conway's little girl", who didn't seem able to grow up or older, marry a man almost a decade of years younger than herself. But Tommy's face looked older, with its sleek mustache, he was tall and walked very proudly down the aisle with little Maggie on his arm after the ceremonies were over. When

they reached the open main entrance of the church the bright rising sun broke through a cloud, flashed on the snow, over the ice-covered trees and dazzled its brilliance into Tommy and Maggie's eyes.

"It's a good omen, Maggie," whispered Tommy.

Then all the admiring friends, who had hurried from the church in order to see the bridal pair come out, saw Maggie smile up at Tommy as if they were aware of nothing but of that "good sign" and themselves.

Maggie's heart was almost bursting with excitement and joy in this new life just begun for her.

PART V

Mountain Brides of Christ

CHAPTER ONE

MIKE MAGANN'S SCHOOL

*G*ENEVIEVE Raebonne was a new girl in the little frame one room school house. She arrived one morning and stood by the door. The teacher was a young Irishman called Mike Magann. Mike was nearsighted and he didn't notice Genevieve standing there by the door. But all the pupils spied her, and especially one, a girl of Genevieve's own size, at least in height—her name was Jeanie Gracer.

Jeanie looked at the poor little girl by the door, with all the pupils eyeing her; but the teacher, so busy writing sums on the blackboard didn't see her at all. Jeanie could stand the suspense no longer. She knew exactly how the strange girl felt. So she slipped out of her seat in the back row and went down the side aisle. She reached the newcomer and whispered to her: "There is a seat by me that is nobody's; come and sit in it." She took the new girl by the hand.

Genevieve followed Jeanie up the aisle while Mike continued to write sums on the board. Then he turned round.

"Now I want all of you to copy them!" he yelled, winking through his thick glasses and thrusting his fingers down his stiff white collar to loosen it a little. "I want every last one of those problems worked before eleven o'clock, and anyone that hasn't done them will feel the sting of my birch persuader." He looked fierce.

Genevieve, seated now, looked at Jeanie in alarm. Even the freckles on her face, and she had loads of them, multiplied under her sudden pallor.

"Don't mind him," whispered Jeanie, "he talks like that but he never hits anything except the stove or the water bucket. He raises a cloud of ashes and splashes water a lot but . . . sh, sh, he's lookin' here!"

Sure enough Mike had spied the new pupil and he came at once to the back of the school room to get information. Genevieve felt creepy and scared.

"So we've got a new pupil," he said slapping chalk-dust off himself, and squinting at her through his glasses. He grinned too. "What's your name?"

Genevieve's freckles began to disappear in the dark pink that now overspread her cheeks so rosy that they fairly shone like apples; the freckles positively went out like stars when the morning comes. Genevieve was perspiring.

Mike saw and had mercy. "Write your name, age, and where you live, etc, etc, etc, etc, on a piece of paper and leave it on my desk," said he, in a hurried tone, for a noisy fight had started behind his back. Two boys were thumping each other.

Mike ran for his persuader. He kept it across the top of the supply cupboard, where the pupils went to get new tablets, pencils, "etc., etc., etc., etc.".

By the time Mike had his persuader the fight was over, but he hit his own desk a terrible crack and threatened again about the problems. As most of the

pupils were good and obedient because their strict
mountain parents had trained them that way, they
were now industriously scratching slates, chewing pencils and heaving sighs.

But Genevieve was bothered: "What was that he
said I was to write besides my name, age, and where
I live? 'Et set' or something?" she whispered to Jeanie,
handing the paper over to her.

Jeanie read: "Genevieve Raebonne, age eleven, live
with my sister, Mrs. Crolley."

"Put 'Tony Crolley's mother,'" suggested Jeanie.
"So's he won't ask you any questions. That's if you *do*
live with Tony's mother."

"Yes," whispered Genevieve, "She's my sister. I'm
Tony's aunt."

"Oh my gracious! Tony's almost as big as you,"
whispered Jeanie.

"Who's doing that whispering?" shouted Mike, pick-
ing up his persuader.

Jeanie gave Genevieve a knowing wink and they
stopped talking. Genevieve looked in despair at her
passport. "Et set" wasn't settled yet. She looked at
Jeanie questioningly and waved the paper a bit.

Jeanie bobbed her head up and down affirmatively
and made her lips show plainly: "It's all right." Then
she tore a piece of paper from her own tablet and
wrote: "Wait till dinner time to put it on the desk; you
better work problems now." She passed the note over
to Genevieve.

Genevieve had brought a tablet and pencil with her
to school and so she set about copying problems for
the sixth grade. It was the highest grade in the school.
When pupils were promoted to the seventh grade they
left Mike Magann's school on the summit and went

down the long hill into the town that lay below, where there was a brick school of many rooms. Each room in this school had its own teacher. Mike's brother, John, taught the most advanced room which was seventh and eighth grades.

So it was up to Genevieve and Jeanie as the only big girls in Mike's school to be exemplary pupils.

Mike retreated to his platform while the problems were being worked. All was silent except scratching pencils. Mike was reading a book. He had ambitions to be a lawyer and probably was getting a bit of studying done.

It was late May and a beautiful warm day. The windows were wide open. Suddenly a voice, hoarse and loud, shouted from outdoors: "Hello there; hello there poppa! Hello there!" The shouting was followed by idiotic laughter in the same hoarse voice. The pupils began to snicker. Mike looked annoyed.

"Hello there poppa!" and more loud laughter came from just outside the windows. Mike got up and ordered all the windows on that side shut. Boys and girls nearest scrambled to close them as if it were a great treat; but first they stuck their heads outside, and all of them were bursting to laugh.

"What is it?" whispered Genevieve to Jeanie.

"A crow," answered Jeanie.

Genevieve looked mystified. She knew all about crows. All they ever said was "Caw, caw, caw!" What sort of place was this where the crows laughed and talked?

Pretty soon it was time to have chart class. Mike laid his book down and said: "Chart class rise."

Little tots scrambled out of tiny desks.

"Pass to class," said Mike.

159

There were about fourteen of them and they formed in a long line in front of Mike's desk.

Mike was standing now, turning over the sheets of a large chart looking for the numbers. The whole school was at arithmetic and the smallest children had to be at that subject also. They were learning to recognize numbers and to count. All in this class were about six years old except the village simpleton, and he was twelve. He never got out of the chart class.

"Here Johnny Snodgrass," said Mike, "Read these figures."

Johnny had a deep bass voice and he liked to use it to hollo loudly, and he *could* count; it was his one accomplishment: "One, two, three, four, five, six," shouted Johnnie. "One, two, three, four, five, six," followed by boisterous laughter, came in the windows from the other side of the room; the crow had settled on another tree: "seven, eight, nine, ten, eleven; ha! ha! ho!—ho! he! he!" The crow could do better than Johnny.

All the school was tense with suppressed laughter.

"Close those windows," shouted Mike, looking now towards the "crow-side" of the room.

They were all closed amid bangs and smothered laughter.

Again Genevieve looked at Jeanie in consternation.

"It's the crow," she whispered, "I'll tell you at dinner time."

The chart class went on with their counting, but now since the doors and windows were tight shut it began to get rather odoriferous in the school. Genevieve was used to fresh air.

"I'm sick," she whispered across to Jeanie.

"Put up your hand and ask to leave the room," whispered Jeanie. Mike's back was turned towards them and they were safe from the persuader threat.

She put her hand up and Jeanie dropped her big geography on purpose at the same time. Mike turned.

"Please may I leave the room?" asked the sick newcomer.

"Yes," said Mike, "but if you talk to that crow out there I'll give you the best trashing you ever got."

Poor frightened Genevieve slipped along the aisle and opened the door into the vestibule. She entered it but didn't dare to open the outside door. Who or what was it out there counting and laughing and talking? A crow? It sounded to Genevieve like the old witch woman who lived along the road to Lillytown out from her home on the Raebonne farm.

Genevieve opened a side window in the vestibule and drank in the fresh air. After that her stomach and head felt better and in a few moments she returned to the room.

All the pupils stared at her in amazement. She wondered why they looked at her so queerly. "Guess its because I'm new," she thought.

"You didn't make the crow talk," whispered Jeanie as Genevieve sat down.

"Chart class turn," said Mike. "Pass to your seats and write your copy."

"First arithmetic class!" Mike sang out. By this time Jeanie and Genevieve were really working at the problems. A window had been opened, for the crow had gone away. It felt like nearly dinner time.

Mike was examining first arithmetic's slates, which they had brought to class. He had a piece of chalk and some were getting one-hundred marks and some were getting zero.

Mike had the other classes, and then he inquired loudly if the sixth grade had finished the problems: "Raise hands who got them all." All hands went up but that of one boy, a terribly fat fellow, who wore glasses and whose dusty hair stood straight up. Mike didn't notice him at all.

By the time it was determined, one by one, that the answers were correct the morning was over.

"Put your books away," shouted Mike.

This command was followed by a small bedlam: slates fell as they were being shoved into over-stuffed desks, pupils talked under the cover of scuffling feet. Other noises were made of so indefinite a nature as to defy analysis or description.

"Pass the caps, Tom Coons," yelled Mike.

Tom rushed to the back of the room, grabbed old ragged and grimy headgear from the hooks and pitched it across aisles to its owners. Each caught his own by leaping up into the air or sprawling over some pupil or desk.

"Pass the girls' wraps, Winnie," shouted Mike.

Winnie in gingham and pigtails stood up and looked back. One lone hat hung by its rubber chin-band on a hook. Winnie went back—she was a fourth grader—and took the hat down and handed it to Genevieve, Jeanie had hung it there. Girls didn't wear hats or wraps in fine May weather.

"Be seated," shouted Mike.

After awhile all were seated, but ready to leap out the door like young lion cubs from a cage.

"Dismissed," commanded Mike. Out of the seats sprang fifty-two young mountaineers of all ages and sizes from five to twelve or thirteen. But even the youngest got through the doors without any serious casualties. There might be a bruised toe or a black eye from the shoving and pushing, but everybody had Sloan's linament at home for bruises, and butter would fix a black eye if the victim hurried home and administered it within ten minutes after it happened.

Genevieve didn't get into the tumult. Jeanie had ushered her up to Mike's desk to deposit her "passport," and now they walked out last, arm in arm. They had never met before but already they were inseparable.

"Now you hurry home," said Jeanie, "and I will, too. Eat your dinner fast, and I'll wait for you here on the school steps. We can talk when you come back, only that I want to ask now if you are going to live at Mrs. Crolley's all the time?"

"Yes," said Genevieve, "I'm going to stay there and go to school. I used to go to the Behe school but it was away over the hills from our farm; I couldn't go when the snow was too deep. Mrs. Crolley just moved to this town."

"Yes I know, and I'm very glad that she has a sister like you. I think we are going to be good chums. I always wanted a chum. What do you like to do most of all?"

"I like to sing, said Genevieve. "What do you like to do?"

"I like to draw and I like to make May-altars. I have a May altar at home now. Have you a May altar?"

"No, I haven't,—I haven't a statue to make one."

"You can use the Blessed Virgin's picture just the same," said Jeanie. "What are you goin' to be when you get big?"

"Oh, I guess I'll be a missis but I haven't decided yet," said Genevieve.

"I'm goin' to be a sister in a convent," said Jeanie.

"Oh, I think that's what I'll be, too," said Genevieve, changing her vocation.

By this time they had reached the cross-roads of the Old Portage and the state turnpike. Mrs. Crolley lived down the pike a little distance, and Jeanie lived right in a corner of the cross-roads. They unlinked their arms.

"I'll wait for you," said Jeanie, "don't forget. Goodbye!" They waved to each other.

Jeanie was delighted, she had a chum at last, and one who changed her vocation from a missis to a sister as soon as Jeanie suggested it. She was going to be a nice agreeable pal. Jeanie told all about her to her mother and two sisters at dinner time. She forgot about the Friedhoff's talking crow she was so enthused about Genevieve. Really they had been so thrilled with meeting each other that both of them had forgotten to bring up the subject of the crow, and all the way home they had exchanged intimate confidences instead. Oh, there were going to be long years ahead together...

Jeanie gobbled her lunch of jelly-bread and milk and then ran upstairs to the May altar. It had a little blue and white statue that belonged to her sister and two little stubs of candles that their mother had given them. It was Cissy's May altar, too. Just now it was overloaded with bunches of blue and purple violets; the little bedroom was filled with their perfume, for the mountain violets are as fragrant as valley lilies.

Jeanie examined the bouquets. Some were half dead in their jelly glasses and bottles. She opened a window and threw them out. She must get more violets before showing the altar to Genevieve. She struck a match and lighted the candles. Then she knelt down.

She was praying hard: "Dear Mother of God, make Genevieve and me into sisters when we are big." She said a Hail Mary. Suddenly she heard a noise behind her. She turned her head, and there was Cissy, her sister, peeping from behind the door jamb and grinning impishly at her. She stopped her devotions and got up from her knees, blew out the candles, and stomped past Cissy, sticking her tongue out at her as she went by. She ran down the stairs and out the front door. She hastened to the school.

None of the girls had come back, but the wild boys were making a racket in the empty field at what they called a ball game.

Jeanie sat down on the lowest step of the six that led to the school-house door. She would wait for Genevieve, who said she'd hurry back. It felt like twenty minutes after twelve. The little ones were coming back. There was Tony Crolley.

"Where's Genevieve, Tony?" called Jeanie.

"She has to 'red' up the table and wash the dishes; mom said so. She's mad, too, and mom says if she don't like it she can go back to the farm."

"Oh," said Jeanie in disappointment, as she got up from her seat, "I guess I might as well go and get some violets."

Jeanie left the school yard and started at a wild running pace down the old Portage Railroad, towards a deep cut. There were no longer any tracks on this railroad, it was the same as any other country road, except that here and there the old stone ties jutted out of the ground. The road was very level and straight. The road between the "cut" towards which Jeanie was going had many years before been one of the inclined planes up which stationary engines had been hauled

165

by great pulleys at the top of the plane; from there
they went on this level road across the top of the mountain, the summit. Jeanie had never seen any of these
marvels. It had all passed away before she was born.
She had heard about it from her mother, who had not
seen it either, but great-grandmother Conway had rid-
den over the mountain on the train pulled by these
engines.

Now in Jeanie's time the "cut" was nothing but a
deep, shady road between two high banks covered with
trees and grass and said to be "ha'nted". A man had
been killed there years and years before; he had gone
to work on the building of the old railroad on the Feast
of the Assumption, without having assisted at Mass
first. After that folks had seen dogs with fire coming
out of their mouths running down the banks of the cut
at night. Once a man, by the name of Criste, had met
a woman in white carrying her head under her arm.
'Twas a fearful place to be after dark. The graveyard
above the right bank, St. Aloysius Cemetery, was to be
preferred, although it was "ha'nted", too!

But white violets grew in the cut, and no place else
that Jeanie knew of, and she loved white violets. So as
frisky as a lamb after her run, she clambered up the
graveyard side of the cut, holding to saplings and trees
as she went to get the very nicest long stemmed violets.

Ha! There near the fence just outside the field
bounding the cemetery was a bunch fit to grace the May
altar of the Queen of Heaven. Jeanie swung to a low
limb and planted her feet on a stone; it slipped and a
shower of loose dirt went scattering. That was nothing. Try again. Jeanie was just ready to put out her
hand and get the bunch, when what crawled out from
under the fence to her right hand, but a big blacksnake,

longer than Jeanie was tall which was about four feet!

Jeanie's eyes almost popped out of her head looking at it. But it never seemed to notice. It looked neither to the right nor the left, but started straight down the stony, grassy, violet-bedecked bank towards the hard road below.

Now it had always been intimated to Jeanie that snakes should be killed. Her father had a lot of rattles from rattle-snakes that he had killed on the Huckelberry Mountain. Everybody killed a snake if they saw one no matter what size it was.

There were plenty of rocks at hand; so Jeanie attacked her duty with vigor. She picked up a medium sized stone and running down the bank after the snake she hurled it at its head. It hit the middle of the snake and pinned it down. From there Jeanie finished her job.

The snake was quite dead, except its tail, "which wouldn't die until the sun went down". Jeanie was triumphant. What a story to tell Genevieve and show her the snake!

Jeanie went to the bank and broke off a stick with which to remove the stones from her victim. She would carry it to school on the end of the stick. Wouldn't the boys eyes pop, the smarties; they could easily see by the tail that it was just freshly killed. This was all passing through her mind while she was removing the stones, when just then two young men, perfect strangers, on bicycles came riding along.

They saw Jeanie with her snake and her stick, removing the stones. They jumped off their bicycles.

"Who killed that?" asked one of them.

"I did," said Jeanie.

They both roared with laughter. Then they began kicking the stones off the snake, and one of them picked it up.

"Whew!" he said; five feet at least."

"Don't take my snake!" said Jeanie, half crying. "I killed it, and I want it."

"You never killed it, kid," said the ugliest one with a slippery black mustache, "you found it."

"I didn't find it *killed!* I killed it all myself," screamed Jeanie. He was putting it across the handlebar of his bicycle and both were mounting to go.

"Don't take my snake," pleaded Jeanie, "I want to show it to Genevieve." She was crying now. "Please don't take my snake."

"Your snake?" They were roaring with laughter. "What do you want with it?" They were riding off now and Jeanie followed them with her eyes. Their shirt waists were billowing out in the breeze as they bicycled swiftly down the road of the "cut" and disappeared as tiny specks far down the plane.

Jeanie looked at the pile of stones and thought of how scared she had been while killing the snake. It had been an awful job. It was the biggest snake she had ever seen and now what was the use of telling about it? The proof was gone.

She felt that it was just about one o'clock. Maybe it was later, she had lost track of her feeling for time. She couldn't stop to gather white violets now; she might be late for school this very minute. Besides she was too excited. But she wasn't breathless. She took to her heels and inside of ten minutes she was at the school.

They were all in, and getting ready to sing.

"Where were you?" asked Mike glowering. He was

standing up in front of his seated pupils with a song book open in his hand.

"Oh!" yelled Jeanie, "I was killing a snake—a great, big blacksnake!" she measured as far as she could reach—"the biggest snake I ever saw! I killed it. Six feet long, about!"

"Where?" Mike was getting interested. All the pupils were agape.

"Down the plane; at the top of the 'cut.' I can show you the stones I used to kill it."

"Why can't you show the snake?" demanded Mike. He must train his pupils not to lie.

"Two men took my snake just as I had it good and dead. But I can show you the stones." Jeanie was still shouting nervously.

"Go to your seat," said Mike, in a snorting manner. The boys were scoffing, too. "Who wants to look at stones? And I hope that none of the pupils in this school will ever tell lies to avoid the sting of my persuader. Now what did I say we'd sing?"

"O Columbia the Gem of the Ocean," they all shouted in unison.

Jeanie got to the back of the room as fast as she could by the side aisle, and sat down beside Genevieve. Pupils were allowed to sit together for singing.

But Genevieve wasn't getting tuned up for her favorite pastime. She was looking sympathetically at Jeanie.

"Did *you* kill a snake?" she whispered.

"Oh, yes," said Jeanie, raising her eyes to heaven. "It was awful—just like the one that gave Eve the apple. But I crushed its head, like Father Barry said the Blessed Virgin did."

"We'll start singing when that talking stops in the back of the room!" yelled Mike, looking at Jeanie and Genevieve.

Genevieve began to get in readiness to tune up. Jeanie got ready to calm down. She would move her lips and pretend to be singing, and have her nerves soothed by "O Columbia the Gem of the ocean".

After school she took Genevieve to her home. She introduced her to her mother, and then they both ran upstairs to the May altar. Jeanie made excuses for the array of empty jelly glasses on the altar.

"They'd have all been filled with white violets if I hadn't had to kill that snake." She had already told Genevieve about the encounter.

She began to fuss about the altar and arrange it. She was taking off the glasses and setting them on the window sill, talking all the while.

"Have you ever been to a church picnic in Rhododendron Park, Genevieve? Its grand when it doesn't rain. We have one on the Fourth of July. How do you spend the fourth out on your farm?" asked Jeanie placing the statue up higher.

"Oh, poppie always gets some shootin' crackers, and we make ice cream. We have ice under sawdust in our ice house. Poppie cuts it in the winter time off the dam. I wish you'd come out with me to the farm sometime, Jeanie."

Jeanie leaped from the altar to sit beside Genevieve on the patch-quilted bed: "Oh, maybe we could go next Sunday!" she exclaimed. "How do we get to your farm?"

"Oh, we walk there. It's not far:—one mile to Cresson, two miles to Munster, straight out the pike, a mile down the lane, and there we are. Four miles."

"I can easily walk four miles. Sometimes Mike's whole school walks down to Father Gallitzin's spring over the mountain, that's a good six miles. I'm a good walker. My great grandmother Conway, was a Cavan racer."

"My goodness! Did she run races like the fellows do at the County Fair?"

"Oh, no," explained Jeanie, she came from County Cavan in Ireland, and they beat all for the way they can walk. My great grandmother always walked to Loretto to Mass, when Prince Gallitzin was pastor. She carried her shoes to save them, besides its easier to walk in barefeet. She put her shoes on when she got near the church; everybody did that."

"Sure I know," said Genevieve, "my grandmother Behe knit socks for Prince Gallitzin; she was one of the ladies that walked in barefeet to church. She put leaves in her bonnet if the sun was hot, so she wouldn't get sunstruck. Poppie puts them in his hat, even yet, when he is out hoeing corn."

"Well, do you think your sister will let you go this coming Sunday?" asked Jeanie, anxious to get the matter of the visit to the farm settled.

"Sure, she will let me go. I'll do a lot of work on Saturday and she will be so pleased she'll say yes. Sunday right after dinner and stay all night. Take your nightgown along.

"Oh, all right!" exclaimed Jeanie delighted. "I hope it's a nice day, because if it rains we can't go walking four miles in the rain."

"Uh huh," grunted Genevieve, shaking her head negatively, "the lane gets awfully muddy in wet weather. You see the cows kick it up a lot coming home every day on it."

"Might we run into the cows?" asked Jeanie anxiously. Her family kept one Jersey cow, called Lily who was bad tempered. So Jeanie was afraid of cows.

"Oh no, poppie has them in another field this month; they come to the barn up the Lillytown road."

"Oh, goody! Then we can go on Sunday."

"Well, I must go," said Genevieve getting up, "Mollie's paperin' and I have to mind the baby. Let's say a prayer first."

"Wait till I light the candles," said Jeanie grabbing up the match box. "Now you make three wishes as this is the first time you've ever been in this church."

Genevieve giggled as they knelt down: "This isn't a church," she said.

"Well, it has an altar and lighted candles; make three wishes anyhow."

"They both knelt and prayed silently. Jeanie took a sly look at Genevieve out of the corner of her eye. Genevieve's hands were folded and her eyes were upturned like a little Bernadette before the Grotto of Lourdes.

"My, she's good," thought Jeanie, who merely got an aspiration said, for Genevieve was making the sign of the cross. Her prayers were over.

"Mollie'll just skin me. She said to come right home after school and here I've been about an hour. What time does it feel?"

"It feels to me about half-past four," said Jeanie; "we'll peep in at the clock when we go downstairs. Tell Mollie I kept you."

Their feelings were correct; it said four-thirty on the old grandfather clock in the corner of the "sittin' room". It was an old clock that Jeanie's mother had knocked down on its face years before, when she was a little girl, but it still kept good time. Genevieve took one look and fled out the door. Jeanie shouted after her: "Ask Mollie about Sunday! Good-bye-e-e!"

CHAPTER TWO

VANITY OF VANITIES

*A*FTER dinner the following Sunday, Jeanie, arrayed in the white dress she had worn to make her first Communion the preceeding Easter, went down to Genevieve's. She felt very fine in that dress. Rich cousins from Wheeling had given it to her. It was very fine lawn with many tucks, ruffles and dainty lace wherever lace could possibly be put. All the little girls in the town had acted suspicious when Jeanie first appeared in that dress. It wasn't the usual medium white lawn, with maybe a bit of common lace at neck and sleeves. It was as fine as silk and a marvel of exquisite hand stitching. Nobody on the summit of the Alleghenies made dresses like that, not even for brides.

"Where'd you get it?" boldly asked Helen Huntsman eyeing it with suspicion and envy.

"None o' your business," answered Jeanie, and immediately all the other girls decided that Jeanie was dressed in an ill-gotten gown.

So Jeanie put on the dress and then her leghorn hat with two pink roses in front and long black velvet-ribbon streamers in the back. She tied her long, curly, brown hair in a bunch at the nape of her neck with a white taffeta ribbon that had been frequently washed and then stiffened with a bit of sugar. It stood up like a butterfly. Her mother often stiffened lace albs for the church that way. Jeanie's mother had a great talent for making her little girls look beautiful.

When Jeanie appeared at Mrs. Crolley's and Genevieve looked at her, she thought she was extremely stylish. She didn't ask any impolite questions about the dress; instead she exclaimed with admiration: "Oh you have such a pretty dress and hat."

Genevieve had a nice plain little white dress with tiny pink flowers dotting it over, such as Jeanie herself would have had, if a rich relation from Wheeling hadn't given her the other. So she knew that she couldn't be feeling snobbish. Genevieve's hat was just as nice, in fact it was almost the same as her own.

It was a great walk out the dusty turnpike, for the month had been unusually dry; but they kept in the grasses along the edges.

A rubber-tired buggy with a man and young woman in it passed them and the two little girls backed close to the rail fence in order not to get much dust on themselves.

"Do you know that fellow and girl?" asked Jeanie.

"Oh, yes," said Genevieve, "that's Patsy Cooney and Tessie Oberhalter. I guess they are going to get married because he's got his left arm around her and he's drivin' with his right."

"Is she going to marry that old fellow with such a big black mustache?" asked Jeanie.

"Oh, they went together at the Behe school; they go along spoonin' like that often. My mother says that's 'sellin' yourself cheap'. Here we are at the lane. Did it seem far?"

"Oh, no, not with all the things we had to talk about. I just couldn't take down all we said. Could you? I keep a book and write down in it the best things that happen to me. I'm going to put this day in it."

Genevieve was busy taking down a bar of the entrance to the lane. They each slipped through easily without soiling their dresses and Genevieve closed the fence. Then they meandered down the lane. It was shaded on each side by trees that grew just outside the fences enclosing the fields on each side. On one side the fence was of split rails and on the other of barbed wire.

Soon they were past all the trees, and the lane was hot, sunny and dusty. They still kept to the side among the weeds and grasses. The lane was very narrow; it would have been difficult for two buggies to have passed each other without one of them going into the wayside weeds.

"My, it's hot for this time o' the year," said Jeanie, stopping to wipe her face with her bit of handkerchief, "and its not June yet." She looked around.

Just then they heard an odd noise, groaning, deep and hoarse, in the distance. It was repeated.

Genevieve stopped and listened intently.

"Oh!" she exclaimed horror stricken; "that's the bull. He's in the lane!"

A moment later they saw him about a quarter of a mile away. He was standing with his head up at attention. Then he gave a great roar, kicked the dust all over himself, and started, head down, in their direction.

"Oh, my dear God and dear Blessed Mother!" screamed Genevieve, "the fence, here under the fence, Jeanie!" She raised the lowest barbed wire and Jeanie crawled under, tearing a yard or more of lace and tucks as she went; her hat crumpled under her.

176

Genevieve got under the same way.

A second later the bull was standing at the very spot where they had made their escape. He had a great triangular wooden collar round his neck. He was big, brown and awful looking. He tried to thrust his head over the fence but the collar prevented.

Genevieve hugged Jeanie frantically where they sat huddled among the grasses and daisies.

"Can he get in here?" asked Jeanie in panic.

"No, he can't—but huddle down till he can't see us, and he'll go away." They huddled.

"Are there any bulls in here, Genevieve?" whispered Jeanie.

"Oh, no! Keep quiet,—he's going away," advised Genevieve.

"Are you sure there are no cattle in this field?" asked Jeanie with her face half smothered in the grass.

"No, no," growled Genevieve, "this is a hayfield. We don't put cattle in a hayfield, but only in a pasture field. He's eatin' grass now; maybe we can go. Let's sit up. They sat.

"He has his head this way. Can he get in if he wants to?" asked Jeanie.

"He'd be in by now if he could," said Genevieve. "Don't you see that he can't with that collar; it's to keep him from jumping fences. Let's get up and walk across the field. It's not much farther. Just over the hill."

They arose. The bull saw them and came again to the fence roaring and trying to put his head over.

"What does he want?" asked Jeanie reassured now about the preventiveness of the bull's collar. "Have you got something to eat with you that he wants?"

177

"Oh I guess that's it. I have two sandwiches here in the poke with my nightgown. Mollie put them in and I forgot. Oh, lookey, the poke's busted. I guess I busted it when I crawled under the fence. Let's eat them and maybe he'll let us alone.

They sat down again and opened the bursted paper bag. Two hard boiled eggs were smashed and a generous supply of salt began to leak out into Genevieve's lap. Bread and lettuce completed the mixture.

The bull now became wilder and seemed anxious to tear the fence down. Jeanie was in terror again lest he'd do just that very thing.

"Oh, I know," said Genevieve hastily looking around in the grass. She picked up a medium sized stone and stuffing it and all the food and salt back in the "poke," she twisted it tight shut, and rising she started running towards the bull.

Jeanie stood up frantic with excitement and fear. When Genevieve got within some feet of the bull she hurled the paper bag over the fence at him. He turned immediately and began to snuffle it. He pawed and snooted until he tore it to pieces and bothered no more about the little girls.

Genevieve ran back to Jeanie.

"Mind you! How he can smell salt; he'll let us alone now. I guess that's all he wanted. But how did he smell it through all that paper? Bulls have good noses I guess.

"Oh, I know!" exclaimed Jeanie, "I'll bet you busted it when we sat on our nightgown-pokes to rest along the pike; mind—when you were tellin' me about the Indian ancestor you had, and the Frenchman?"

"Yes, I guess I busted it then, and the salt was spillin' out. Cattle go crazy for salt."

"Oh, I'm trembling all over. I can hardly walk", said Jeanie, "but let us go over the fields as you said."

They set out again and soon came to a rail fence dividing the field they were in from another one. They crawled over it. Jeanie's dress was now dirty and torn, her face and hands were begrimed, and her hat was bent—her beautiful leghorn hat. Genevieve was not nearly so dirty; she had thrown her hat over the fence before she crawled under to escape the bull.

They were now in a pasture field; the grass was low, for cows had grazed there.

"We can cut across this field 'catty-corner,' " said Genevieve, and get in the lane again; the bull can't come past the lane bars that are close to our house."

They were going diagonally now across the field towards an old stake-and-rider fence.

"Do we have to crawl over that fence, too?" asked Jeanie forlornly. "How many more fences have we?"

"Just this one that we're coming to," answered Genevieve soothingly.

As they were going towards the fence that led into the bull-less portion of the lane, Jeanie heard a cow moo. She looked to her right and over the brow of the hill she saw a whole herd of cattle grazing.

"Oh, Genevieve," she screamed, "look there!"

"They are only cows, and we haven't any salt now; but hurry up anyway."

They fairly ran, and soon were at the fence, Jeanie got on top of it first, and looked around. Sure enough, bars were across part of the lane and the bull was behind them.

They were again in the lane. Jeanie was sorry that she had come, but there was nothing to be done about it now. This was a far worse adventure than killing the snake. But she must not hurt Genevieve's feelings; she must pretend that she enjoyed it...

In a moment they saw a little streak of blue smoke and then a chimney and roof.

"There's our house," said Genevieve.

"Well, let's sit down and rest a minute in this shade," said Jeanie, "I'm all tuckered out, and look at my dress. You are not half so dirty. But I guess we should be thankful to be alive. If that bull had mauled you to get the poke of salt! Are you ready to die, Genevieve?"

"Yes, I think I am. I always say my prayers and I was just at confession last week. I never do any big sins. Are you ready?"

"I don't know. I'm so scared of hell. I don't think I have any real big sin either, but they say purgatory is just as bad as hell and lasts terribly long, even for venial sins. I have some of them. I get mad and tell people to mind their own business. I stick my tongue out, and once in a while I tell lies. I said I tore my brown dress on a nail when I really tore it on a bush."

"What did you tell that for?" asked Genevieve laughing, "wasn't a bush as bad as a nail to tear it on?"

"Oh no, because I wasn't allowed to go in the bushes with that dress on. It was my Sunday dress and I went to the woods in it on Sunday. You see I'm disobedient, too."

"Yes," said Genevieve; "and who did you stick your tongue out at?"

"I stuck it out at the Huntsman's girls. They ask spiteful questions and are 'gape-seeders.' "

"What do they ask, for instance?" inquired Genevieve.

"Well, they asked me where I got this dress—now you never asked me that."

"I don't think its any of my business," said Genevieve, looking at the dress: "It *was* a pretty dress."

"Yes, but look at it now. My rich cousins gave me this dress and my mother had it fixed over a little. My cousins have lots of money. Their father is a doctor and he's famous for cutting people up and taking things out of them, like tumors and such. He's grandpap's nephew. Grandpap was rich once, too, when he was president of the brick works, but after that he got poor and even had to sell hickory brooms for a living. His father had been a duke and lived in a castle in Germany."

"What's a duke?" asked Genevieve, chewing on a long grass stem.

"Oh, something like a king but not nearly so high, and not quite as high as a prince. You know Father Gallitzin was a prince. A duke has loads of money and is a close friend of a king."

"Why did your great-grandfather stop dukin'?" asked Genevieve only slightly interested.

"I don't know that. I'll find out sometime I guess. But grandpap says it was all for the best. That's how things pass away in this world. Well, the doctor, grandpap's nephew, has charge in a big hospital in Wheeling. Some people call him "the old butcher" but if they have any ailments that need cut out they all want him to do it. He charges a lot. He has whiskers and looks old but he makes lots of money. He has four girls and this was Ida's dress. Now you know where I got it, but don't you tell anybody. Do you think I can fix this lace where it's torn off?"

"Sure, you can sew that. It'll never be noticed. I'll lend you a dress and mommie'll wash this one for you to go home in."

"Will I have to go back by the lane where the bull is, or else crawl over all those fences?"

"Of course not," said Genevieve, scornful of such a stupid question; "I'll ask poppie to put the bull in the barnyard when we are going back. They weren't expectin' visitors today. I should o' sent a postal card. Poppie goes every day to the R.F.D. box at the head of the lane. Are you rested enough to start out again?"

"Oh I guess so but I'm ashamed of the way I look, after I took so long to fix up. But that's the way it is in this life..."

They got up and traveled onward. Soon they were at the gate that opened into the yard around the old farmhouse that had belonged to ancestors back at least five generations. The house sat on the side of a hill and a great green bank was just beside the kitchen door. The gable of the house faced the gate which made the front porch seem to be at the side. This porch was two stories high, a balcony porch above and one below. A well worn path ran around among shrubbery to the entrance.

As the two little girls entered the gate a big black dog rushed out and jumped up on each of them in turn. His dirty paws made more grimy marks on Jeanie's dress. He was barking with glee and licking Genevieve's face.

Jeanie was in a hopeless state of dishevelment when at last they arrived at the steps.

Mr. and Mrs. Raebonne had been disturbed from their Sunday afternoon nap by the barking of the dog and now they were standing waiting to see who had arrived. Mrs. Raebonne came forward while Mr. Raebonne was busy scolding the dog for being so wild and impolite.

"Genevee, dear," said Mrs. Raebonne, smiling and kissing her, "What a surprise!" Then she kissed Jeanie in all her grime, welcomed her gladly and called her "Daughter" just the same as Genevieve.

Genevieve was already engaged in telling the story of the bull, and poppie was laughing loudly and promising to put him in the barnyard the next day when they would be returning up the lane. They had dilly-dallied so much on the way that it was after four o'clock; Mrs. Raebonne departed for the kitchen, saying she had to begin getting supper.

Genevieve sat in her mother's chair and talked to her "poppie". Jeanie insisted on sitting on the porch step and resting herself against a pillar; she had her back to Genevieve and she meant to shut her eyes and get a nap.

Genevieve was telling all about Mollie and the children, the papering, and the housekeeping. Poppie was talking about the planting he was doing, and why he had the cows in that field and the bull in the lane. Genevieve was telling about school, saying that she liked it better than the Behe school. She said Mike acted cross but wasn't, and she thought he was smarter than Algy Horne, who taught the Behe school.

Jeanie was listening as in a dream. Here she was out on this remote farm! Not a house in sight; just hills, hills, valleys and woods off there to the right; crows cawing; sheep bleating down there in that shadowy place near a clump of trees and some shining water.

It was almost June and the sky was a lovely blue with not even a white cloud to liven it up. This May was like July. How could Genevieve live in such a lonely spot? She felt dreadfully sleepy; she leaned her head against the pillar and went into a doze.

She was awakened by Mrs. Raebonne calling them to supper. There were just the four of them, for the rest of the children were away with married ones, where it was easier to get to school.

After supper they sat on the porch again and talked about everything. Genevieve described Jeanie's May altar. Jeanie told about the snake she had killed and they all believed her. Genevieve told her parents that she was going to be a sister when she grew up and her poppie and mommie gave their consent right then and there. Mrs. Raebonne told stories about the time when she was a girl and lived on this farm with her brothers and sisters. Mr. Raebonne told about his boyhood on the adjoining farm. It was all merged into one farm now and the grandparents were dead.

It began to get dark and the stars came out; frogs began to croak and cheep from the glistening pool down near the clump of trees. Mr. Raebonne made the air pleasant with the odor of his pipe. He was saying nothing in his deep contentment. Pretty soon it got very dark and the clock in the house struck nine. Genevieve proposed that she and Jeanie better go to bed.

Mrs. Raebonne lighted a kerosene lamp and gave it to Genevieve. Then she kissed them both: Genevieve first and then Jeanie. "Goodnight Jeanie, daughter," she said.

Halfway up the stairs Jeanie inquired: "Does your mother always kiss you goodnight?"

"Not every night," said Genevieve, "she misses some nights."

"We don't do any kissin' in our family," said Jeanie in a tone that she tried to make sound superior; but as she was doubtful it didn't ring true. She already loved Mrs. Raebonne.

Genevieve led on up the creaking old stairs to a bedroom whose door led out onto the balcony porch. She set the lamp down on a dresser decorated with flounces of pink and white calico. Pictured saints were plentiful on the walls; the Blessed Virgin with the Child and St. Joseph with his lily had the most prominent places and the largest frames. They were brilliantly colored; you couldn't miss seeing them, even though the lamp didn't give much light.

Jeanie got out of her begrimed dress and put her night-gown on. She removed her shoes and stockings, untied her hair and ran to the door:

"I'm going to say my prayers out here on the balcony," she said.

"Wait and I'll say mine there, too," called Genevieve, who was tugging at a shoestring of her high fourteen lacers.

Jeanie waited kneeling by the balcony rail and looking up at the stars. She thought now very decidedly of being a sister. No bulls would get after you if you were safe in a convent. No snakes would meet you and need to be killed. No schools like Mike's with dirty, wild boys to tease and scoff at you and not believe when you killed a snake bigger than any of them ever killed. You'd not need to tell lies and stick your tongue out at 'gape-seeders'. Sisters were all like saints. Just like Blessed Margaret Mary in the picture at home with Our Lord showing her His Sacred Heart.

Genevieve came out and knelt down.

"Let's say our prayers out loud," she said.

"All right," answered Jeanie.

"In the Name of the Father," they began. They

knew the same prayers and said all of them; they ended up with a very fervent act of contrition. After that they knelt looking at the stars.

"I'm going to really be a sister, too, when I get big," said Jeanie. "I know for sure after today. I always think things are going to be so good and they nearly always turn out something like today. Nothing's really any good on this earth. I want to go to heaven for sure."

"So do I," said Genevieve. "I like to pray. Don't you?"

"I'm not so crazy about praying. Sometimes I have them all said and I was thinking about something else all the time. Don't you do that?"

"Oh, no, when I pray I just love God and His Blessed Mother. I don't think of anybody else."

"You must be a saint," said Jeanie bluntly. "Come on to bed, I'm dreadfully tired."

CHAPTER THREE

GOING TO BE A SISTER

*G*ENEVIEVE was sixteen; she would be
seventeen in January, but this was only
September. Jeanie was already seventeen
since the August before.

They had long since finished the eighth grade at
John Magann's school, and the next year John had gone
away to Philadelphia to study law with his brother
Mike. A new man had taken John's place. Never
again would there be such interesting teachers as John
and Mike Magann.

But school was all passed for there was no high
school in the town. Grammar school ended one's education. It was time to plan what to do with one's life.
Genevieve was getting to be quite determined to be a
sister. But the great problem was: what convent? She
did not know any Sisters. Neither she nor Jeanie had
ever been inside a convent in their lives. Would Sisters
take her? How did one go about the business?

About a year before, a Sister of Charity from a convent in Westmoreland had come to the mountains to
visit her cousin, Mary McGarrity, who lived all by her-

self on the old McGarrity farm. This sister had been the very first girl from the summit of the mountain to go away to be a nun. Her name had been Susie Brown and now she was known as Sister Victoria. Mary McGarrity was a kindly old maid and a first cousin of Jeanie's mother. A thousand wrinkles were criss-crossing on Mary's face, but she had beautiful sparkling grey eyes and a tiny treble voice. She was always very eager for news.

Whenever Mary's cousin, Sister Victoria, and her companion sister came to see her about once every few years, it was a great event. Mary stood on the steps of St. Aloysius church the preceeding Sunday and told all her relatives and friends; it was a great distinction for Mary. Mary also hired a woman to come and give the house an extra cleaning, to bake a fine cake, kill a couple of chickens, wash and iron the linen tablecloth and napkins, shine the silverware, that was never used for anything else—not even for Christmas—and to make all sorts of preparations for Sister Victoria and her companion, who would be there for only a day!

So when Mary McGarrity stood on the Summit church steps one Sunday after Mass and waited for Jeanie a great event was about to happen!

"Jeanie," said Mary, plucking her by the sleeve as she came out the church door; "Sister Victoria and another Sister are coming on Wednesday. Tell your mother; and maybe you'd like to come out to the farm and meet her. Bring your drawing book; I'd like Sister Victoria to see the pictures you can make."

"Oh, all right!" exclaimed Jeanie; "Sisters! Two sisters! I'll be tickled to death, Mary. Thank you for asking me, and I'll bring my book. I'm so sorry Genevieve is out on the farm, maybe I could have brought her along?"

Mary didn't say anything to that; she had never met Genevieve and so wasn't interested.

Jeanie understood at once and was glad Genevieve was not at Mollie's just then, for she couldn't go without her, neither could she take her along unless Mary invited her.

On Wednesday Jeanie hurried out to McGarrity's farm all alone. The road was not so lonely as in the years gone by when Jeanie's mother went that way with Mary's brother Charlie. There were a few houses along the road now.

It was a red letter day and one to be written in her book—the day that Jeanie met the sisters! She was allowed to see exactly how they dressed in the convent, when they took off their big crepe bonnets and long shawls. She saw at close range the little black shiny caps with a fringe of hair showing below; the neat cape with its sharp creases, the chained rosary and brass crucifix. They were Mother Seton Sisters of Charity, Jeanie's mother had said.

The little sister with Sister Victoria was very young and pretty, but she was not a mountaineer. Sister Victoria was beautiful and so calm and dignified. She walked so stately and when she sat down in a chair she did it with such grace that Jeanie was rapt in admiration. No wonder cousin Will Conway, years before, went out and wept when he saw Susie Brown's lovely braid of dark brown hair that she had given to Mary after she had it cut off in the convent. Jeanie felt as if two saints had stepped down from heaven. She didn't dare show her drawing book—but Mary did.

"Bring out your book, Jeanie, and show it to Sister Victoria," said Mary.

The pictures were enthused over. Sister Victoria said they showed a lot of talent, and then she asked Jeanie what she intended to be.

"I want to be a sister," said Jeanie at once.

Then followed questions; Sister Victoria was really interested and so was her companion. Jeanie told how she had always wanted to be a sister.

"Well, we'll see about it when we go back to Westmoreland," said Sister Victoria.

When the happy day was over and Jeanie came home, she told all about what had happened and how she was going to be a sister.

"You don't know your own mind", said her mother. "Such a sudden notion! What do you want to be a sister for?"

Now Jeanie had never talked pious or told her thoughts on the vanity of life and the things of this earth, except to Genevieve. Cissy would surely snicker, and her mother would think she was just posing a bit. So Jeanie told one of her lies.

"Sister Victoria says I have talent for drawing and they would maybe make an artist-sister of me." Jeanie just couldn't tell her real reason.

"That's not the right motive," said her mother decisively. "An artist indeed! People don't enter convents in order to be made into artists. I knew you didn't know your own mind. That ends it. Don't talk about it any more."

When Jeanie's mother spoke in that tone of voice Jeanie knew it was all over. Jeanie's mother had been little Maggie McDermott and she was now firm and determined like her old grandmother Conway before her.

That night Jeanie knelt by her bed and cried. If she had only told the truth about her thoughts on the vanity of life. Wasn't that what she and Genevieve always talked about. She had never even thought about the old drawing book. It had been Mary who brought up the subject. She had a big notion to tear it to smithereens and never draw another scratch. Now things were all twisted and even if she did try to explain to her mother she'd probably think she was making up a pious tale so she could go to the convent to be an artist. It certainly was all over. Did one never have a pleasant thing happen in this world without its getting spoiled in the end?

Nobody ever told his inmost thoughts in Jeanie's family. Cissy had snickered when she caught her praying in front of the May altar. Still everybody was pious and the walls were covered with holy pictures. But being a sister was now all over. Jeanie took a good cry and gave it up.

During the next year and a half Jeanie didn't know what to do with herself and was only completely contented when she was with Genevieve.

It was in the following September Genevieve again brought up the subject of being a sister with a firm determination to do something about it.

"I guess I'll go to Lillytown and see the Sisters of Saint Joseph. I'm called Genevieve after one of them. I'll go next Sunday."

"Don't be a Sister of Saint Joseph, be a Sister of Charity; that's what I'm going to be sometime," said Jeanie dubiously.

"When are you going? You never talk about it any more," said Genevieve impatiently.

"Oh, I don't know; but in my bones I know it will happen," said Jeanie.

"Well I can't be fooling; I want to do it right now: next Sunday. It's in my bones, too, but I'm gettin' it out," said Genevieve.

So that was settled: Genevieve was going to Lilly-town to find out how to be a Sister of Saint Joseph and wear a long graceful veil, black habit with wide flowing sleeves, white around her face, and look like a saint.

But Providence intervened. Sister Victoria happened to make another visit to her cousin. Jeanie had not heard about it. Neither had she ever talked any more about wanting to be a sister. The truth of the matter was that a boy was interested in Jeanie and she was playing the flirt. It was a cause of great annoyance to her family. She hid boxes of candy with big bows of red ribbon on them; she received picture-post cards by the dozen and had an album to keep them in; she had a locket around her neck which, according to her stories when compared by different members of her family, no less than five different boys had given to her!

Genevieve, on the other hand was very pious and good. She flirted with no boy. After confession on Saturday afternoon she wouldn't talk but went straight home to Mollie's and after supper she went to her room and prayed until bed time. She spoke to no one when she was preparing to go to Communion. She didn't want to have the tiniest speck on her soul. She meant to be a sister and that meant to be a saint headed for heaven.

Mary McGarrity told Jeanie's mother that Sister Victoria was coming. She didn't even invite Jeanie over to see the sisters. But everybody knew that Genevieve was about to go and be one as soon as she found a convent to take her.

"Jeanie," said that young lady's mother, "Sister Victoria is coming again to Mary McGarrity's on Thursday. You should take Genevieve to meet her. I told Mary that I would send her with you. Maybe she'd like to be a Sister of Charity."

"She's going to Lillytown on Sunday to see about being a Sister of Saint Joseph. She has her mind made up," said Jeanie uninterested.

"Well it won't hurt for her to meet Sister Victoria; besides I told Mary and she'll be expecting the two of you."

It was the first week in November and the roads were already frozen when Jeanie and Genevieve journeyed out to McGarrity's farm. There were no fences to be climbed over or bulls to be encountered: the way was clear for both of them.

Sister Cecelia was with Sister Victoria; she had been Maisie Schwab from Loretto, a mountaineer like themselves. Her brother Charley was a millionaire, a "steel king", people said, but Maisie was a nice happy Sister of Charity.

There were no drawing books to be shown this time. Genevieve was the center of interest and it was strictly a business meeting. Genevieve sat up very pertly and determined and told that she'd like to enter as soon as possible.

Sister Victoria promised to send her the questionaire, and if everything was satisfactorily answered she

194

could enter on the first of January. Sister Victoria was a member of the superior's council and in that capacity she could speak with authority. As Sister had been a mountaineer herself, she personally knew Genevieve's parents and even her grandparents, and so there were no inquiries necessary into heredity and family respectability.

Jeanie felt sad, and more so when she understood Sister Victoria's lack of interest in herself. She had received a letter from Jeanie's mother two years before telling her that Jeanie didn't know her own mind and wanted to be a sister only because she thought the Order would make an artist of her.

Sister Victoria and Sister Cecelia were very polite to Jeanie but their affection seemed all settled on Genevieve. Jeanie kept quiet. She never mentioned her lost vocation at all. She'd help Genevieve to attain hers first and then maybe God would provide for her.

About a week later Genevieve received the papers. She and Jeanie filled them out and sent them off to Westmoreland. Shortly after, word came that Genevieve was to come to the convent for a personal interview with the superior. It was late November when she boarded the train and went by herself the whole seventy miles. It was her first long trip by train, and all alone! She stayed two days.

Oh, what thrilling tales she had for Jeanie when she returned! She had descriptions of the entire convent. She had met the girls who were now learning to be sisters. They wore little lace caps and black dresses. The novices dressed in brown, and wore shiny brown caps. There were about twelve of them, and oh, they were all so happy and good!

Genevieve was fairly incoherent with enthusiasm.

Then began the dressmaking and sewing for her convent wardrobe. Mollie cut and stitched while Genevieve gladly minded the baby, got the meals, washed the dishes, sent the boys to school and sang all the time. She sang all the hymns she knew and repeated them over and over again.

Jeanie spent almost every waking minute at Mollie's house watching the progress of the wardrobe. At last the day came for Genevieve to depart. The trunk was locked and strapped and taken to the railroad station to be checked on Genevieve's ticket. She had spent a week at the farm, and now she stood with Jeanie and Esther, another girl friend, waiting for the train. It was the last day of December.

Jeanie and Esther were going along, and Jeanie was to remain a week with her mother's cousin, Will Conway and his family in Westmoreland. Esther would return to the mountain the very next day.

Jeanie and Esther sat in the convent parlor waiting. The Mistress of Novices and Sister Victoria had come and taken Genevieve away with them, and they had not seen her for about an hour. At last she returned and she had a little black lace cap on her head and a short cape over the shoulders of the black dress that Mollie had made. Genevieve was a postulant!

Jeanie and Esther remained all night and heard the whistles and bells of Westmoreland welcome the New Year. It was a pleasant novelty to hear all that clamor at midnight! It sent delightful thrills up and down their spines as they sat up in bed behind white curtains and talked to each other.

Next morning there was a grand High Mass for the Feast of the Circumcision of Our Lord. Afterwards the convent rang with the singing of "Happy New Year to You." All the Sisters were joyful and smiling.

Genevieve appeared, and said farewell to her two friends: "I'll pray Jeanie that you get here, too," were her final words. Esther had other plans: she was soon to be married. Jeanie was still flirting—but Genevieve knew all.

Jeanie stayed the following week with her cousins. The first Friday arrived and as Jeanie had a special devotion to the Sacred Heart of Jesus and used to look at the picture of Saint Margaret Mary and wish to be a sister, she went with the Conway girls to confession. Here she met with a pleasant surprise. She would never forget it, nor *that* confessor.

When she came out of the confessional her mind was made up: there would be no more flirting and she would follow Genevieve as soon as possible.

It was a bleak mountain top to which Jeanie returned the Sunday after New Year's. But the following days were worse; there was no one to tell intimate things to any more.

Then letters began coming from Genevieve, happy, joyful letters. Jeanie answered and begged her to pray that she could come too.

Now, Jeanie had disturbed her parents and her older sister so much with her flirtations that they would have been relieved had she taken such a notion as Genevieve's. But she never mentioned the convent any more. Hadn't her mother told her to never bring the subject up again?

One day a letter came to Jeanie from Genevieve, and

in it she advised her old chum to write to Sister Victoria and tell her the truth of why she wanted to be a sister. Genevieve also said that she had told Sister Victoria that Jeanie had always wanted to be a sister and didn't care about the old drawing book at all.

So off to her room went Jeanie and locking the door, she wrote the letter and mailed it herself. She told no one.

She received an answer within the week: "Come not later than Holy Saturday," was the principal sentence. Enclosed was the questionaire and the wardrobe list.

Jeanie walked straight to her mother. "I'm going to enter the convent for Easter Sunday," she said. "Here are the things I must do: I must get a doctor's certificate as to my health, I must get the pastor's letter of recommendation and fill a trunk with the things on this list and answer these questions. Her mother read the letter, looked at the papers and then sat down on the end of the old lounge to ponder a bit. Jeanie had certainly been acting foolish; her mother hadn't noticed it much since Genevieve went away, but no telling when she might break forth again. Now here she was bringing up the subject of being a sister, as she had two years before.

"Maybe it would have been better if I had let her go the first time," thought Mrs. Gracer. This time she didn't ask her daughter to tell her her motives.

"Well, Jeanie," she said, "I have on objections if you still want to be a sister. I'll not put a thing in your way, and I'll help you all that I can."

It was Holy Saturday and a wet gloomy day when the old wagonette and two grey horses stopped under the porte-cochere at the convent in old Westmoreland.

Out of it stepped Jeannie. She heard voices above her and looking up she saw Sister Victoria and a novice leaning over the stone balcony railing.

"Oh, there is Regina," said Sister Victoria with great pleasure in her genteel voice.

Down the steps flew the novice in her brown habit, and Jeanie was almost smothered in Genevieve's arms.

THE END